MODULAR SCIENCE
for GCSE

MODULE *Energy*

Spread

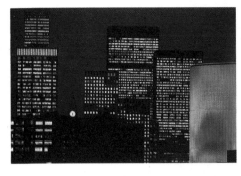

*In any process or change, **energy** is transferred. Energy is being changed from one form to another all around you in the natural and technological world. This module looks at energy in all its forms, where we get energy from and how we use it today.*

*Relevant National Curriculum
Attainment Target: 4*

1 What is energy?

The reason for change

Energy is needed to make anything happen – it makes the sun shine, it makes cars and buses move, it even keeps you alive!

For something that is so important in our lives, energy is very hard to explain. We know we have to 'save it' if we want to keep our bills down. We know that the glucose in a Mars bar is 'for energy'. If somebody is very active, we might say that they are 'energetic'. But exactly what is energy? Where does it come from? What kinds of energy are there? Whatever it is, it certainly comes in a lot of different disguises!

Energy helps you work, rest and play!

The sun sends out **light** energy and **heat** energy.

Fridges remove **heat** energy from food. This makes the food cold.

Gas contains *stored* energy. This turns to **heat** energy when you burn it.

Electric lights give out **light** energy and **heat** energy.

Food contains *stored* energy.

Petrol contains *stored* energy.

1 Make a list of all the different kinds of energy shown in the three scenes on these pages.

2 For each of these kinds of energy, try to list the ways in which we can use them.

3 Write a sentence or two to explain what you now think energy is!

If you looked up the word 'energy' in a science dictionary, you would find something like 'energy is the capacity to do work'. But what does work mean? Work in this sense can mean making anything happen.

Energy is often stored in energy sources, such as fuels and batteries. But in many cases the energy from these sources is changed into another form of energy before it is used. Whatever form it's in, energy is useful stuff. You can find out more about energy by reading through this module.

2 Active energy, stored energy

Lots of energy

Though there are many different types of energy, it is possible to sort energy into two main forms. Some types are **active** and so are more obvious. Light can be seen, sound can be heard, heat can be felt. A moving object clearly has energy, too.

But where is the energy in a piece of coal, a sausage, a wound spring, a battery or a rock on a hillside? The energy here is **stored**, and only appears when something happens to make it *change* into active energy.

From stored to active

Potential energy is stored in the rock due to its position at the top of the hill.

As the rock rolls down the hill, its potential energy changes to kinetic energy.

Some stored energy is called *potential* energy because it has the '*potential* to do work'. For example, things that are high up have **potential** energy. If they are not held in place they will fall downwards because of the pull of gravity. As they fall, they lose this potential energy, which is turned instead into energy of motion, called **kinetic** energy.

Other energy 'stores'

Energy can also be stored in things that have been bent, squeezed or stretched.

A bent bow has stored energy – when it is released, this turns into the kinetic energy of the moving arrow. This is similar to the energy stored in a stretched spring or elastic.

The wound spring in a clockwork motor stores energy in much the same way. A spring metal strip is coiled tightly by winding a key, or by turning the wheels. When released, the metal tries to straighten out. This releases the stored energy, causing the wheels to turn – releasing kinetic energy.

Because these ways of storing and releasing energy all involve *mechanisms*, this type of stored energy is called stored **mechanical** energy.

Stored chemical energy

Some materials have energy locked up in the chemicals from which they are made. Perhaps the simplest example of this is coal. A lump of coal may not seem very energetic, but just try burning it to make it react with the oxygen in the air! A lot of energy is given out in the form of **heat** and **light** energy. Materials like this – such as wood, coal, oil and gas – are called **fuels**.

The food we eat reacts in a similar way inside our bodies. The energy released keeps us warm and also provides the energy we need for life – food is like a fuel for our body!

At a barbeque, chemical energy stored in the charcoal is released as heat energy. The cooked food also releases its stored chemical energy – inside your body.

Batteries also contain stored chemical energy, but this time the chemicals react to give **electrical** energy. This is a particularly useful type of energy as it can be easily turned into many other types of energy, such as light, sound, heat...

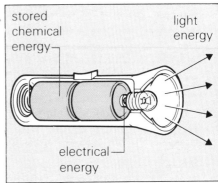

From active to stored

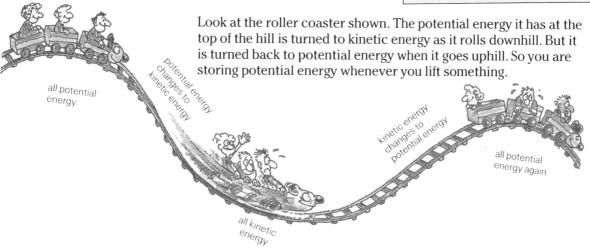

Look at the roller coaster shown. The potential energy it has at the top of the hill is turned to kinetic energy as it rolls downhill. But it is turned back to potential energy when it goes uphill. So you are storing potential energy whenever you lift something.

A similar process happens in a car, but involves electricity. When a lead-acid (car) battery is connected to the headlamps, the energy stored in the battery is turned into electrical energy and then into light energy. But once connected to a battery-charger, electrical energy is pushed back into the battery, refilling the energy store!

1 List some examples of active and stored energy.

2 What are **two** main types of stored energy? For each, try to explain how the energy is stored.

3 What type of energy does stored mechanical energy usually turn into?

4 What types of energy can stored chemical energy turn into?

5 How can active energy be turned back into stored energy?

3 Electricity – simplicity!

Non-stop energy

As we have seen, the different types of energy can be changed from one to another. In fact, when we say we 'use' energy, it is not 'used up', it is simply changed from one form to another. Energy cannot be created or destroyed – it can only be released or stored.

Some changes are easier to achieve than others and special devices are often needed to make the change. Electrical energy is generally the easiest form to change, which is why we use so much of it!

Energy can never be lost – it just changes into a different form. But it is easily wasted!

The electrical merry-go-round

For every device which changes electrical energy into another form of energy, there is usually another device which can convert that energy back into electrical energy.

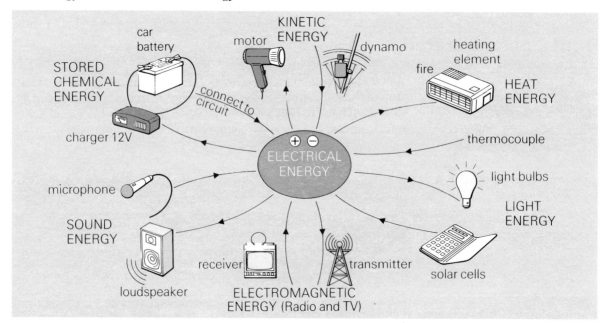

Measuring energy – the joule

A 1000 W fire uses as much energy each second as ten 100 W light bulbs.

Unlike distance or time, energy is not usually easy to measure – there is no simple 'energy' equivalent of a ruler or stopclock! The unit of energy is the **joule** (J). One joule is about the amount of energy needed to lift a small apple from floor to table top. However it is possible to work out the energy used by electrical equipment fairly easily.

If you went out to buy a light bulb, you could choose from various bulbs, such as a 60 or 100 watt bulb. The number of watts tell you how bright the bulb will be. These figures are a measure of the **power** of the bulb – this is the rate at which things use energy. For every **watt** of power, *1 joule of energy is being used every second*. So a 100 W bulb uses 100 joules of energy per second.

Power to the people!

In an industrial country like Britain, there is a large demand for electricity. In all, there are 81 **generating plants** (power stations) in Britain. That's enough to keep over 500 million light bulbs constantly lit.

Although these generating plants use different energy sources, most of them use a long 'energy chain' like this.

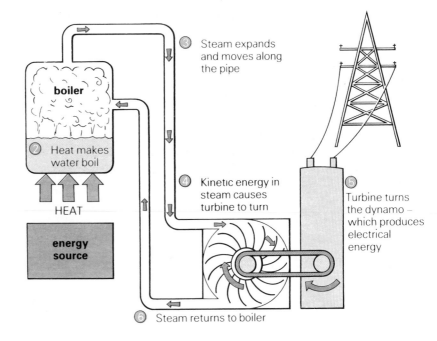

③ Steam expands and moves along the pipe

boiler

② Heat makes water boil

HEAT

energy source

④ Kinetic energy in steam causes turbine to turn

⑤ Turbine turns the dynamo – which produces electrical energy

① The stored energy in the energy source is released as heat energy

⑥ Steam returns to boiler

But is it efficient?

The trouble is that every energy change is less than perfect. Not all the energy released by the energy source ends up as electricity. A lot ends up as 'waste heat' which never reaches the turbine. For every 100 joules of 'stored energy' that start the journey, 70 joules are wasted and only 30 get as far as your home! Because of this, electricity, though very useful, is an expensive way for us to get our energy!

Household waste?

Once the electrical energy gets to our home, do we waste it too? The answer is yes and no. An electric fire can be very efficient – producing 95 joules of heat from every 100 joules of electrical energy. But the humble electric light bulb is an efficiency disaster – only 5 joules of light energy from every 100 joules of electrical energy – the rest is heat! That's why you may need gloves if you have to change a bulb after it's been on for a while! Fluorescent tubes are much more efficient – 20 joules of light energy are released by every 100 joules of electrical energy. That's why your school uses them.

A light bulb produces a lot of heat – which is no use to see by and it may hurt too!

1 Why is electricity such a useful form of energy?

2 What is the unit of energy? How much energy is used by a 60 W bulb every second?

3 Describe and explain the basic 'energy chain' used in a power station.

4 Why does only such a small amount of the original 'stored energy' end up as electricity?

5 **a** Why do schools tend to use flourescent tubes rather than light bulbs?
 b Write down three reasons why people prefer to use light bulbs at home?

4 Supply and demand

Keep going, don't stop

Electrical energy is very useful, but it is expensive to produce. One reason for this is that oil- or coal-burning plants have to be kept running 24 hours a day! If shut down for anytime, the boilers have to be cooled slowly and carefully to avoid damage. A period of maintenance is then needed, followed by an equally slow warm-up period when they are put back into service.

The National Grid

Over a long term, the slow cooling and start up of plants is not too much of a problem. This is because Britain has an energy 'highway' system – the **National Grid**. For example, as overall demand falls in the summer, a plant at Southampton can be shut down for a few months. In the meantime that region can 'feed' off the rest of the National Grid.

'I want it now!'

The main difficulty in organising a national distribution of electricity is the ever-changing demand for electricity. At night, most of the country stops work, goes to bed – and demand for electricity drops like a stone!

But the generating plants can't just be switched off, so what can be done with all the 'surplus' electricity at night? There are two main ways of tackling the problem – either use more electricity at night or build power stations that respond more quickly.

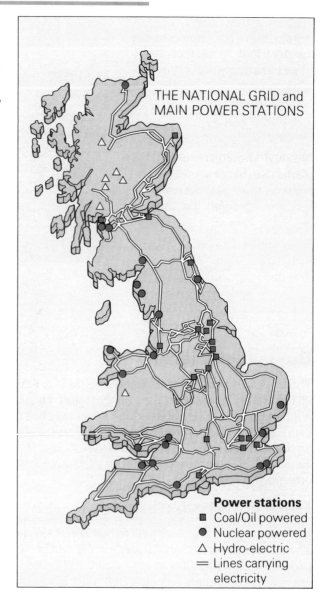

THE NATIONAL GRID and MAIN POWER STATIONS

Power stations
- ■ Coal/Oil powered
- ● Nuclear powered
- △ Hydro-electric
- = Lines carrying electricity

Buy now, use later!

As many people use electricity for home heating, it's a good idea to try to store the electricity as heat. **Night storage heaters** are connected to a separate payment meter that only works at night. Because electricity is plentiful at night, it is sold off at 'bargain' rates! Night storage heaters use this cheap electricity to heat up special bricks inside the heater. This heat stays stored in the bricks all through the night. This stored energy is then slowly released into the house the following day. But despite plenty of publicity, this has not really made much of a dent in the problem. This is because the main demand for electricity is when people are awake – working, cooking and watching TV. There is no way most people will do these things all night instead!

Hydroelectric plants

These do not use an energy source which produces heat – so they do not have long cool-down and warm-up periods.

Water high in the mountains has lots of potential energy which turns to kinetic energy as it flows downhill. This can be harnessed to turn turbines, spin dynamos and so produce electricity.

In countries with high mountains and lots of rain, like Scotland and Wales, high valleys are often dammed and their water is chanelled through pipes to turbines to generate electricity.

A hydroelectric plant can be shut down or started up in minutes rather than days so they are very useful plants to include in the National Grid. Hydroelectric plants in mountainous areas of Britain can be used to supply electricity all over the country. Another advantage to these plants is that the rain comes free! So not only are they flexible but they are cheap to run too!

High valley dammed to form reservoir.

Water from reservoir turns turbine near bottom of dam.

Turbine turns dynamo, generating electricity.

Pylons take away electricity generated by dynamo.

The natural conditions here in the north of Scotland – high valleys, plenty of rain – are ideally suited to the building of hydroelectric plants like this one. Other areas also have natural conditions which can be used to generate a lot of electricity in a similar way. Tidal estuaries, windy plains and hillsides are examples of such safe sources of power.

1. How are long term changes in the demand for electricity coped with?

2. Why are the short term changes (day/night) such a problem?

3. What are the energy changes that take place in a hydroelectric plant? Draw a simple energy chain diagram to show all the changes.

4. 'What use are night storage heaters? They heat up at night, when I'm already warm in bed'.
How would you convince this person that such heaters are useful?

5. Explain why a hydroelectric plant is a useful type of power station to include in the National Grid.

5 Pumped storage systems

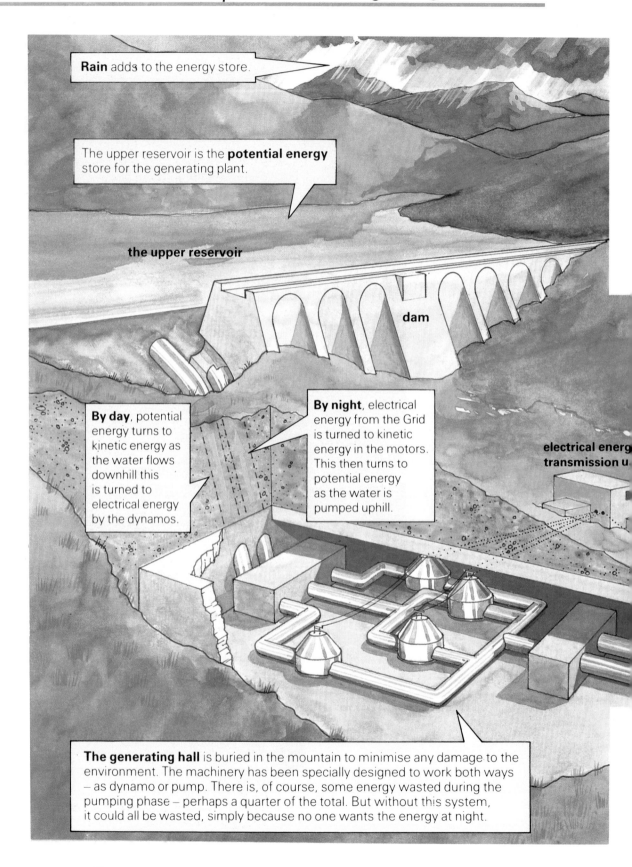

Rain adds to the energy store.

The upper reservoir is the **potential energy** store for the generating plant.

the upper reservoir

dam

By day, potential energy turns to kinetic energy as the water flows downhill this is turned to electrical energy by the dynamos.

By night, electrical energy from the Grid is turned to kinetic energy in the motors. This then turns to potential energy as the water is pumped uphill.

electrical energ transmission u

The generating hall is buried in the mountain to minimise any damage to the environment. The machinery has been specially designed to work both ways – as dynamo or pump. There is, of course, some energy wasted during the pumping phase – perhaps a quarter of the total. But without this system, it could all be wasted, simply because no one wants the energy at night.

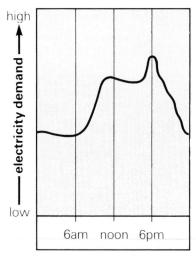

At what times will sudden increases in demand mean that the National Grid will need electricity from Cruachan?

A combined effort

Recently, various projects have brought together hydroelectric plants and a new method of storing electrical energy. Take a closer look at one of these projects. . .

The Cruachan Dam holds back a vast lake high in the hills of Argyll, Scotland. This is the potential energy storehouse. It is added to by rainfall over the hills (which is common!) but it also has another way of filling.

During the peak daytime demand in electricity, the plant acts as in a 'traditional' hydroelectric plant. Water falls through tubes the size of railway tunnels to the generating hall – a great cavern cut from solid granite deep in the mountain. There it is used to drive the special turbine-dynamos which then feed electricity into the National Grid – all within minutes of starting the plant up.

But the water does not flow away – instead it is kept in a lower reservoir. At night, the National Grid is full of surplus electricity, but few people are awake to use it. Now the machinery goes into reverse. The turbine-dynamos become motor-pumps which push water back up into the upper reservoir – storing some of the unwanted electrical energy as potential energy. This water can then be used to generate electricity in the normal way – such as during the next day when everyone is awake and at work.

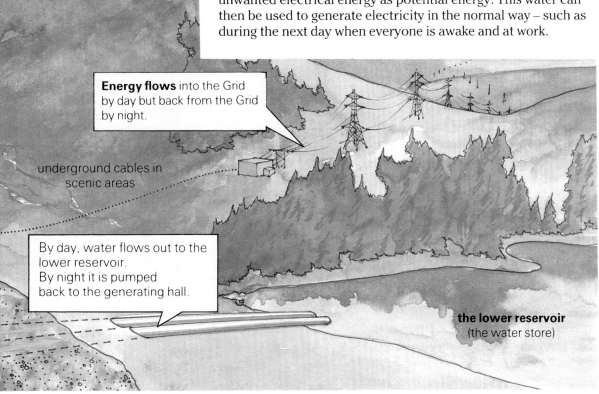

Energy flows into the Grid by day but back from the Grid by night.

underground cables in scenic areas

By day, water flows out to the lower reservoir.
By night it is pumped back to the generating hall.

the lower reservoir
(the water store)

1 List all the energy changes involved in turning the potential of the water in the dam into electrical energy.

2 You are an engineer who wants to build a pumped storage plant in the mountains, but local people fear that you would damage the environment. Set out your case for building the plant. Explain briefly how it will work and why it is needed. What steps will you take to protect the environment?

6 Heat and temperature

Getting into hot water!

'Don't touch it, it's hot!' – a common enough warning at dinner time. Everyone knows what it means. But people often get confused over the difference between heat energy and temperature.

Heating things up

If we put heat energy into something (by burning a fuel or using electricity), it gets hot – its temperature rises. **Temperature** is a measure of how hot something is. But a given amount of heat energy does not always produce the same rise in temperature if different materials are heated.

Some materials need to absorb more heat energy than others to give the same change in temperature. The amount of material being heated also makes a difference.

A full kettle will take twice as long to boil as a half-full kettle.

Heat, temperature and moving energy

If we talk about the amount of **heat** energy that an object has, we are actually describing the amount of **'internal'** energy that an object has. This depends on what the material is, how much of it there is, and how hot it is. One way to think of *temperature* (hotness) of an object is as a description of how *concentrated* that heat energy is in the object.

In a bucket of cold water, the heat energy will not be very concentrated – yet the total amount of energy in the whole of the bucket will be quite large. A sparkler 'spark' is very hot and so its heat energy is very concentrated – yet there is only a tiny amount of material in the spark – so the total amount of energy is small.

So which way will energy flow if a spark lands in the water? In fact, the spark 'loses' energy and cools down (a lot) while the water gains energy and warms up (a little!). This cooling and warming carries on until they are both at the same temperature. Heat energy *always* flows from hot things to cooler things until they are both the same temperature.

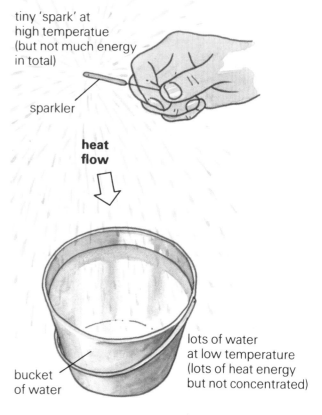

tiny 'spark' at high temperatue (but not much energy in total)

sparkler

heat flow

lots of water at low temperature (lots of heat energy but not concentrated)

bucket of water

What will happen when a spark hits the water?

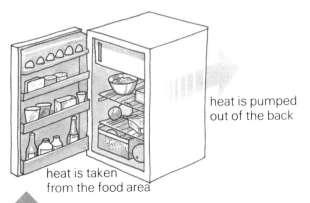

heat is pumped out of the back

heat is taken from the food area

Fridges feel warm at the back as heat energy taken from the food is released.

How do things get cold?

The simple answer is by passing on their heat energy to other objects. If there is some way of *continuing* to pass on heat energy, then a cold object can become even colder.

A fridge does this by circulating a cooling fluid inside the fridge. This fluid keeps coming back to remove heat energy from the food – so the food becomes cold.

Measuring temperature

Though we can feel if things are hot or cold, this is not very accurate. Our senses are easily confused – a cool swimming bath feels warm if you've just had a cold shower! We use **thermometers** to measure temperature accurately.

A typical thermometer is made from a thin-bore glass tube with a reservoir bulb at one end, full of mercury (or coloured alcohol). If the bulb is heated, the mercury **expands** (gets bigger). The glass also expands, but not as much as the liquid. The expanded liquid pushes up into the tube. The hotter it gets, the further it goes – if it cools, it **contracts** (shrinks) back down the tube.

The tube is marked with a scale by marking the points for melting ice and boiling water (taken as 0 degrees and 100 degrees), and dividing the rest of the tube evenly between these **fixed points**. This is called the **Celsius** scale, after its inventor. Each point on the scale differs by one degree **centigrade** (°C).

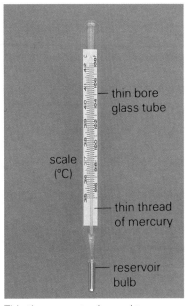

thin bore glass tube

scale (°C)

thin thread of mercury

reservoir bulb

This thermometer is used to measure body temperature. If this is too high or too low, a person is ill.

Why we get cold

Our normal body temperature is 37°C – that's hotter than the hottest summer day! A warm room is at about 20°C, so even then our bodies constantly lose heat to 'warm the room'. We replace this heat loss with heat from our fuel – food! The more the temperature drops, the more we have to use up our food to keep our body at 37°C. Sometimes our muscles do a little extra work to help this – by shivering. But if it gets too cold, we may not be able to generate heat fast enough and our temperature will fall below 37°C. This is called **hypothermia** and can be fatal – especially for the old or very young.

1 Which would boil first over the same flame – a full kettle or one that is only half full?

2
  a Which has more heat energy, a sparkler 'spark' or a bucket of water?
  b What happens if they meet?

3 Describe how a simple thermometer is made. How is a scale added?

4
  a Why do we shiver when cold? What good does it do?
  b Suggest different ways that we can keep our temperature at the correct level.

7 Heat energy on the move

How heat energy moves

Given enough time, heat energy will flow from a hot place to a cool place until the temperatures have levelled out. How long it takes for this 'levelling' to occur will depend on the **temperature difference**, and also on the **materials** involved. Some let the energy flow quickly; others slow it down. To understand how best to use them, we first need to know about the three ways in which heat energy can move: **conduction, convection** and **radiation**.

Heat moves in three different ways – which one will make these balloons rise?

Conduction

When you first prod a fire with a metal poker, one end could get 'red hot' while the other end stays cool enough to hold. But after a while, the heat energy moves steadily along the poker, each bit of material being heated in turn by its neighbour. This is the way heat passes through *solids* – it is called **conduction**.

Metals are generally good **conductors** – and some are very good. A copper 'poker' would give you burnt fingers in minutes. Not all solids are good conductors. Plastic and wood are used as saucepan handles because they do *not* conduct heat well. Poor conductors are called **insulators.**

boiling
water at
100°C

gauze to
trap
ice

ice at 0°C
does not melt

A metal soon conducts heat all along its length – but liquids are very poor at conducting heat. The hot water at the top cannot transfer heat to melt the ice.

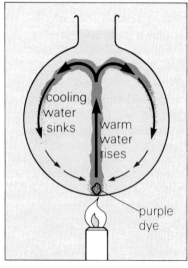

cooling
water
sinks

warm
water
rises

purple
dye

Liquids are very good at carrying heat upwards – but by convection, not conduction.

Convection

Although liquids are poor conductors, they will let heat travel in a different way. This happens when a liquid (or a gas) is heated from below. First the liquid at the bottom is heated directly by *conduction*. This *hot* liquid **expands** and 'floats' up through the cooler liquid.

When the hot liquid reaches the top, far away from the heat source, it cools. More hot liquid (rising from below) pushes the cooling liquid out of the way. The *cooling* liquid now **contracts** and starts to 'sink'. Back at the bottom, it is heated once more and starts to rise again. . .

This process is called **convection** – and this flow of liquid is called a **convection current.**

Radiation

Conduction and convection both need a material which can transfer heat energy – solids for conduction, liquids or gases for convection. So how come we feel heat from the sun, which reaches us through 150 million km of the empty vacuum of space? The answer is that the energy reaches us as **infra red radiation**, which is like light and radio waves. You can feel these infra-red waves when you warm your hands in front of an electric fire. **Microwaves** are very similar, but they have the neat trick of penetrating your dinner and heating inside and out at the same time.

By directly heating the inside of food, microwaves cook food very quickly.

Home heating on the move

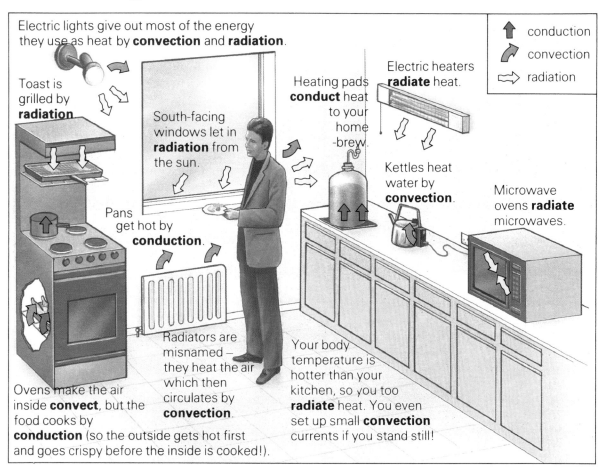

Electric lights give out most of the energy they use as heat by **convection** and **radiation**.

↑ conduction
↗ convection
⇨ radiation

Toast is grilled by **radiation**.

South-facing windows let in **radiation** from the sun.

Heating pads **conduct** heat to your home-brew.

Electric heaters **radiate** heat.

Kettles heat water by **convection**.

Microwave ovens **radiate** microwaves.

Pans get hot by **conduction**.

Radiators are misnamed – they heat the air which then circulates by **convection**.

Your body temperature is hotter than your kitchen, so you too **radiate** heat. You even set up small **convection** currents if you stand still!

Ovens make the air inside **convect**, but the food cooks by **conduction** (so the outside gets hot first and goes crispy before the inside is cooked!).

 What are the three ways in which heat can move?

 a What materials (if any) are needed for each heat transfer?
b Describe how the heat energy moves in each case.

3 Why can't heat from the sun reach us by conduction or convection?

4 List examples of conduction, convection and radiation that you use in your home.

8 Stopping heat from moving

plastic/cork – good insulator, doesn't conduct heat away; stops convection of hot air above liquid; blocks radiation.

double-walled – allows vacuum to be made.

hard case – protects fragile glass walls.

vacuum – no solid, liquid or gas, so there is no conduction and convection.

hot drinks stay hot

(or cold drinks stay cold)

silver surfaces – reflects radiation back into flask.

seal point – where air was removed when making vacuum.

A vacuum flask can keep heat in – or keep it out – by stopping conduction, convection and radiation.

Marathon runners can get very cold when they stop running. 'Space blankets' help to stop them radiating heat.

Stopping convection

Like any gas, air is a very poor conductor. If it can be stopped from moving around (and so convecting), air can make a good and cheap insulator. That is how clothes and fur help to keep us and animals warm. Even the tiny hairs on our bodies stand up when we're cold, to try to trap more air and so keep us more insulated. A similar effect is given by air trapped between the sheets of paper used to wrap our fish and chips.

Other natural insulators, such as cork, trap air in tiny pockets or bubbles. Expanded polystyrene, fibre glass, string vests and foam rubber all insulate in this way – so does corrugated cardboard, as used by all the best tramps!

Don't waste it!

Heat energy is only useful if it can be kept where it is wanted. If heat energy moves away from such places, it is wasted – and this can be expensive!

To insulate properly we have to stop all three methods of heat transfer. The classic example of this is the vacuum flask.

Stopping radiation

Silvery surfaces do not absorb heat radiation – they reflect it, just like a mirror reflects light. They are **poor absorbers** of heat. The larger the area of the surface, the more points there are from which it can radiate heat. Silvery surfaces are very smooth and flat. Rough surfaces have small scratches – these expose more of the surface. This means rough surfaces can radiate a lot of heat, but silver surfaces do not. So silvery surfaces are **poor radiators** of heat.

That's why your Chinese take-away stays hot in its shiny aluminium container – the inside surface doesn't absorb much heat from the food, and the outside surface doesn't radiate much heat out.

'Space blankets' are thin silvery plastic sheets. These can help to keep in your body-heat if you are out in cold weather. They can also help old people beat hypothermia (see page 13).

Another way of *stopping* radiation is to *avoid* using **black surfaces** – these are very **good radiators**. They are also **good absorbers**, that's why a black coat feels hot on sunny days.

The fur of the arctic fox slows down convection – and its white colour reduces heat loss by radiation too!

Insulating materials for the home

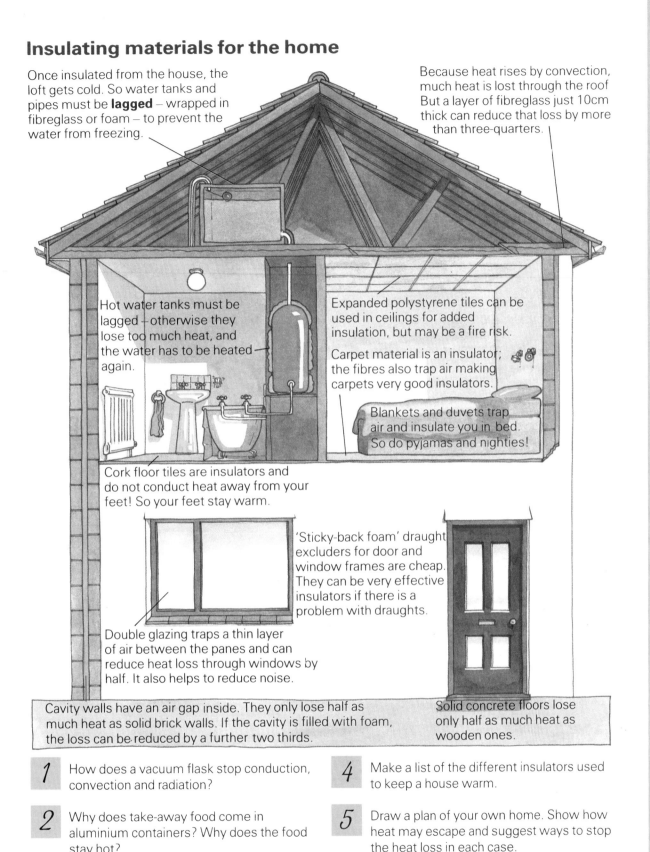

Once insulated from the house, the loft gets cold. So water tanks and pipes must be **lagged** – wrapped in fibreglass or foam – to prevent the water from freezing.

Because heat rises by convection, much heat is lost through the roof But a layer of fibreglass just 10cm thick can reduce that loss by more than three-quarters.

Hot water tanks must be lagged – otherwise they lose too much heat, and the water has to be heated again.

Expanded polystyrene tiles can be used in ceilings for added insulation, but may be a fire risk.

Carpet material is an insulator; the fibres also trap air making carpets very good insulators.

Blankets and duvets trap air and insulate you in bed. So do pyjamas and nighties!

Cork floor tiles are insulators and do not conduct heat away from your feet! So your feet stay warm.

'Sticky-back foam' draught excluders for door and window frames are cheap. They can be very effective insulators if there is a problem with draughts.

Double glazing traps a thin layer of air between the panes and can reduce heat loss through windows by half. It also helps to reduce noise.

Cavity walls have an air gap inside. They only lose half as much heat as solid brick walls. If the cavity is filled with foam, the loss can be reduced by a further two thirds.

Solid concrete floors lose only half as much heat as wooden ones.

1 How does a vacuum flask stop conduction, convection and radiation?

2 Why does take-away food come in aluminium containers? Why does the food stay hot?

3 Why do tramps often wrap themselves in cardboard boxes and newspaper when "sleeping rough" in the cold?

4 Make a list of the different insulators used to keep a house warm.

5 Draw a plan of your own home. Show how heat may escape and suggest ways to stop the heat loss in each case.

9 Energy in the home

What's it used for?

The main uses of energy in the home are for heating, lighting, cooking and for electrical appliances. The electrical appliances you use are up to you. But in Britain, everyone needs some form of heating, lighting and cooking. And there is more than one way of doing each.

Hot house

Long ago, rooms used to be heated by an open fire in each room. But each open fire let a lot of heat escape up the chimney. So **central heating systems** were developed. These used just one source of heat – such as a boiler heated by **gas**, **oil** or **coal**. Only one chimney is needed, a special one which does not allow much heat to escape. The boiler heats water which then flows through pipes to radiators. These radiators then warm up each room. The water then goes back to the boiler to be heated again. Most boilers also heat up a separate supply of water for the hot taps.

Electric central heating is not really central heating – it uses separate night storage heaters (see page 8). Each heater produces heat from its own supply of electrical energy – there is no central source of heat energy. Hot water for taps comes from a water tank heated by an electrical **immersion heater**.

An alternative to central heating is to use *individual* sources of heat – such as a fire (coal, gas or electric), a fan heater or a portable heater (electric or gas). The kitchen or bathroom may have a wall-mounted water heater. These sources are often more suitable for a particular room than a radiator would be. They are frequently used to give extra heat, in addition to a central heating system.

Light bills?

For a particular amount of electricity, fluorescent lights (strip lights) give out four times more light than electric light bulbs. But many people do not like to use them in their homes – and choose to use the less efficient electric bulbs. This is because lighting does not form a big part of their energy costs.

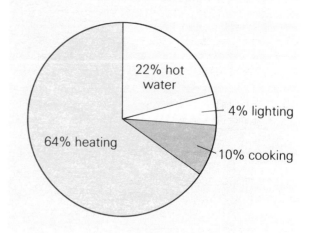

Energy used in the home for heating, cooking and lighting.

coal
(cheap)

needs regular 'top ups' and cleaning, pollution risk from mines, soot and gases

oil
(cheap)

easy to use, pollution risk from oil slicks

natural gas

very cheap, but not available everywhere, no pollution

LPG

'bottled gas', cheap, portable, no pollution

electricity
(cheap at night)

expensive by day, easy to install, pollution risk from acid rain, nuclear waste

Different fuels used in the home.

Making a meal of it

There are many different ways of cooking – using an oven (gas or electric), a grill, a pressure cooker, a slow-cooker, a toaster, a microwave oven and so on. Each method has its advantages. Microwave ovens are very efficient at cooking food in small amounts, or which contains a lot of water. If lots of food is to be cooked, then a conventional oven may be more cost-effective. You just have to choose a method that suits your needs and your purse!

Cheap, quick and effective insulation – draught excluders.

Hidden insulation – foam can be injected to fill the hollow cavity in most home walls.

Spend money to save money!

It costs money to produce the heat energy needed to warm a home. In time, all of this heat escapes – that is why a home eventually gets cold. If any of this heat escapes too quickly, then money is wasted along with the heat. So even a small reduction in the amount of heat wasted can mean big savings.

Let's consider a home with a heating bill of £300 a year*. If 10% of the heat can be kept in for longer, then the heating bill will be reduced by £30. But how much money should be spent on insulation? It all depends on which type of insulation is chosen. . .

Heat escapes through. . .	Percentage of heat escaping	Cost of heat escaping*	Possible insulation	Reduction in heat escaping	Cost of insulation	Years to recover cost	Comments
Walls	35%	£105	foam in cavity walls	35%→14%	£315	5	needs experts
Roof	25%	£75	fibre glass in loft	25% → 5%	£180	3	cheap, easy to do
Draughts	15%	£45	draught excluders	15% → 6%	£54	2	very cheap, very easy
Windows	10%	£30	double glazing	10% → 4%	£216 or £1800	12 or 100	do-it-yourself or expert fitted

More than just money

There are other considerations besides the cost. Many people like to have open fires instead of modern forms of heating. But a central heating system can be operated by timers which make heating a home very easy and convenient – the choice is yours!

1 Why is central heating so called?

2 Which form of insulation is cheapest and easiest to put in?

3 Make a list of the advantages and disadvantages of the different types of home heating.

4 If you had £400 to spend on insulation, how would you spend it? Explain your answer.

10 Fuels: from boom . . . to bust?

The good old days

For hundreds of years, coal was a very important fuel. Not only could it be used for heating, but it was also the source of many chemicals for industry. By the 1960s, coal had been replaced by **oil**. Oil was used in power stations, for petrol, for plastics . . . the list of uses was very long indeed.

Many countries rode the crest of the 'cheap energy' wave, thanks to the glut of oil from the Middle East. People who suggested we were wasting a very precious resource were laughed at . . .

How cheap was cheap? Find out how much 7/6 (7½ shillings) is in pence. How much is petrol now?

The crisis

Then, in the early 1970s, the main group of **o**il **pr**oducing & **e**xporting **c**ountries (OPEC) limited oil production and fixed a higher price. They realised that they only had a limited amount of oil to sell. They had to make it last and get as much money for it as possible.

In countries like Britain which imported a lot of oil, the result was economic chaos. Petrol prices rocketed. So did the cost of electricity because oil was used in many power stations. Industry used vast amounts of oil too, so the 'knock-on' effect of high oil prices pushed up the price of many other goods.

An OPEC conference – these representatives of the main oil producing countries can decide the price for oil world-wide.

Fuels last longer and bills get smaller if you 'save it'!

The need for conservation

With this rise in the price of oil suddenly it became very important to use less fuel and save money. In the '70s cars began to be designed and sold for their 'fuel economy' rather than their 'performance'. People became more aware that the **fossil fuels** (coal, oil and gas) would soon be used up and could not be replaced. In the short term there was only one thing to be done – try to 'save it' – try to economise on our comsumption of fuel to make what we had last longer.

The good news . . .

In Britain, because imported oil was now dearer, it was worth spending more money to look for it! Billions of pounds were spent searching for oil in the rocks beneath the **North Sea**. Very soon this money was pouring back into the economy when the North Sea oil rigs started to produce high quality oil. By the early 1980s, Britain had more than enough oil to use at home and became an oil exporting country!

Drilling for oil – the precious 'black gold'.

. . . or is it?

But by 1985 things began to totter. The energy-saving campaign, coupled with the general industrial slump, meant that there was a lower demand for oil worldwide.

At the end of the year, the OPEC countries failed to agree to reduce their production evenly. Once again there was an oil surplus – and prices fell drastically. The energy consumers of the world were pleased. Petrol could go down in price, electricity might be cheaper, lower fuel costs would be 'good for industry' and so would help the economy. . .

The only problem was that Britain was also an oil exporter. Falling oil prices meant getting less money for the oil we sold.

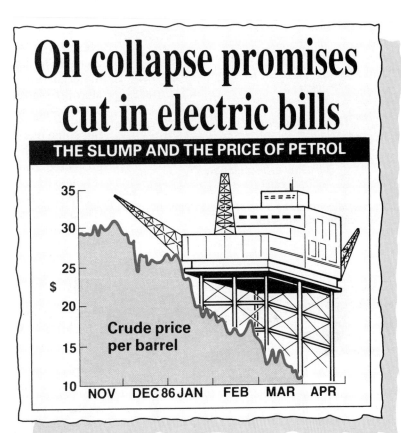

Oil collapse promises cut in electric bills

THE SLUMP AND THE PRICE OF PETROL

Crude price per barrel

(NOV DEC 86 JAN FEB MAR APR; $ 10–35)

What next?

Eventually the oil will run out. The flow of North Sea oil is already slowing down. So where will we get our energy supplies from? **Nuclear** energy is one possibility but so are **alternative** energy sources. As importantly, where will we get a new supply of the chemicals we obtain from oil? One source is plants, using **biotechnology** to extract useful chemicals. Another source, which should last for 300 years is **coal**. Back to where we started!

1 Suggest five ways that we could all save energy.

2 It is easier to use the oil we have now than it is to find new oil supplies. Do you agree? Explain your answer.

11 Coal

Plants – natural energy stores

We use plants as 'body fuel' (**food**) but we also rely on them as sources of energy for our technological society. In the simplest form, we burn **wood** from trees to keep us warm. The trees have energy (from sunlight) stored in the complex chemicals that make up wood. By reacting these chemicals with oxygen – burning them – we can get back some of that 'sunlight energy'.

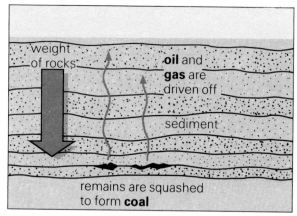

Great heat and pressures deep in the Earth transformed buried plant material into coal.

Fossil fuels – ancient energy stores

This process of 'trapping sunlight' has been going on for millions of years. Most of the plant material formed in this way broke down soon after the plants died. It then released its energy to bacteria and fungi that cause decay.

But some plant material became trapped in sediments. This material was sealed in and protected from total decay. This material has retained its trapped energy – until now, when we dig up this **'fossil'** material and use it as fuel. When we burn fossil fuels – **coal**, **oil** and **gas** – we are releasing the energy store that was built up by plants, using sunlight, millions of years ago.

Millions of years in minutes!

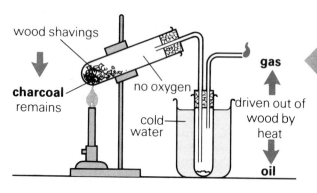

This experiment shows how fossil fuels might have formed when plants (and animals) were buried by sediments, millions of years ago.

Wood is heated in a closed container, away from the oxygen that would make it burn.

As the wood is heated, any liquids and gases in it are driven off and the complex chemicals break down. What is left behind is charcoal – almost pure carbon. Coal must have formed, deep underground, in a similar way.

British coal

Britain is very lucky in having large coal reserves. This is because about 300 million years ago, it was largely covered by great swamp forests. Rivers rushing from mountains in the north poured sediment into the area, burying great areas of forest that had sunk beneath the water. This process was repeated many times. Eventually the forests were crushed and the many British coal fields were formed.

From soft plants to hard rocks – powerful cutting machines are needed to remove the coal.

From plants to coal

It has taken 300 million years of deep burial to turn the swamp forests' trees to coal, but plant material has collected in a similar way ever since. How much this material has changed depends on how old it is.

Peat In the moorland areas of Scotland and Ireland, the remains of *thousands* of years of 'bog moss' have been compacted to form **peat**. This soft brown material still shows traces of tougher roots and leaves. It is cut with a spade and allowed to dry, and then used as a fuel (as well as being spread on gardens!). It is not a very high grade fuel, though, as it burns at a low temperature and leaves a lot of ash.

Lignite This is older plant material that has collected over the last *100 million* years. It has been compressed more than peat, and has had more of its 'volatiles' driven off. What is left is a brown, soft, waxy material called **lignite**. This can be cut into thin strips and burnt like a candle. This 'halfway' coal is found in Yugoslavia and Greece and a large deposit is now being mined beneath an Irish loch.

Bituminous coal This is typical 'household' coal. It may be hard, dark and shiny, or soft and powdery. Often it is a streaky mixture of the two types. It has a much higher carbon content than lignite, and needs to be given a 'kick' of energy to get it burning. Once it is burning, it produces a hot, but smokey flame.

Anthracite This is a very 'high-grade' coal (nearly pure carbon) that is found where coal seams have been folded or heated deep in the Earth. It is hard and shiny and doesn't mark the hands. **Anthracite** is also hard to light but, once lit, burns with a very hot and smokeless flame, leaving little ash. For this reason, it is used in solid fuel central heating systems. It can also be burnt in **smokeless zones** (such as London).

---

1 Where did the stored energy in fossil fuels originally come from?

2 Why has Britain got such a lot of coal?

3 Describe the differences between Peat and Anthracite.

4 If peat were buried for 300 million years, what might it end up as?

5 **a** Which type of coal must be burnt in smokeless zones?
   b Why do you think it is necessary to have smokeless zones?

12 Oil and gas

A long time coming

Oil and gas were produced over millions of years from dead plant and animal materials. These materials often collected at the bottom of ancient seas and were covered by layers of sand and mud. This prevented them from decaying – instead, great heat and pressure broke the materials down into **crude oil** and **natural gas**. The tiny droplets of oil and bubbles of gas rose through sponge-like **porous rock** like sandstone. In some places, they kept on rising until they reached the surface. The black oil collected there as a black sludge.

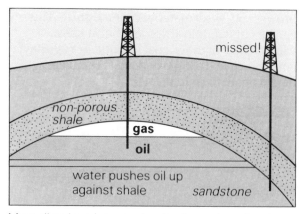

Oil was first found at the surface.

Black sludge to black gold

Nobody bothered with it until 1859 in Pennsylvania, USA where it was discovered that the black sludge could be made into a good substitute for the whale oil used in lamps. Soon people began drilling all over for the crude oil. By **purifying** the sludge, different parts could be used for heating, lighting and water-proofing. Soon it was in demand as a fuel for cars. The oil rush had begun! Nowadays, oil is also used to make plastics and other useful chemicals.

Most oil and gas is trapped under dome-shaped rocks.

Oil traps

Once all the oil near the surface had been used up, scientists had to look for it deeper in the ground. Sometimes the dead plant and animal material had been covered up by mud millions of years ago. This mud eventually formed **non-porous shale** which trapped the oil and gas. All the scientists had to do was to find the right rock formation, drill a hole and pump up the oil and gas. Sounds easy, but it costs millions to drill one well – and only 1 in 40 wells turn out to be in the right place!

The many dome shapes on the surface of this area suggest oil may be below – the many small oil wells confirm it!

What's it good for?

Each fossil fuel has different uses – but most involve releasing the energy locked up in the fuels. During burning (**combustion**), this energy is released as **heat** and **light** energy. For example, a flame is just a collection of hot gases giving off light energy. As well as heating homes, the heat energy can be used to make gases expand in engines. These gases push on pistons, in the engine, **making the machine move**.

What happens during burning?

Oil and **natural gas** are made up of chemicals called **hydrocarbons**. These contain various amounts of **hydrogen** and **carbon**. When they are burned, the chemical energy stored in the hydrocarbons is released as light energy and heat energy. It is not always easy to start the reaction – a small amount of heat is needed to get things going. Usually a spark or flame is enough. Once it is burning, the fuel itself can provide the energy needed to keep the reaction going.

One fossil fuel – **coal** – is *not* a hydrocarbon. It is almost pure **carbon**. It burns to give only carbon dioxide, plus light and heat energy. Sometimes other chemicals are present in the fuel. These produce **pollutant gases**, such as **sulphur dioxide**, which can cause acid rain. If there is not enough oxygen, the fuel does not burn properly and a poisonous gas called **carbon monoxide** is produced. This is why it is important to keep fires well-serviced and well-ventilated.

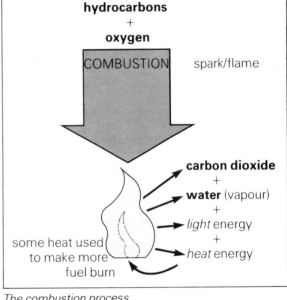

The combustion process.

What's the difference?

Solid, liquid and gas fuels burn in different ways. . .

Coal – most is 'hidden' inside the lump, away from air. Burns with air only on surface, so takes time to get hot enough to keep combustion going.
Made from tightly packed carbon, each lump releases a lot of energy.

burning coal

Oil, petrol – if sprayed in small drops, it burns quickly. Burns with air on surface of *each and every* drop. Together, drops soon release enough heat to make fuel burn quite quickly. Liquid fuel may also form a vapour which can burn very easily. Not as tightly packed as coal, so releases less energy than small volume of coal.

burning oil droplets

Gas – mixes very quickly with air. Rapidly releases enough heat to keep gas burning. Not at all tightly packed, so large volume needed to release a lot of heat.

burning gas

1. What are the three main uses of crude oil?

2. Why do oil and gas collect under shale?

3. Why is a spark or flame needed to start a fire?

4. Water can absorb a lot of heat. Suggest a reason why water can put out a fire.

13 Other sources of energy

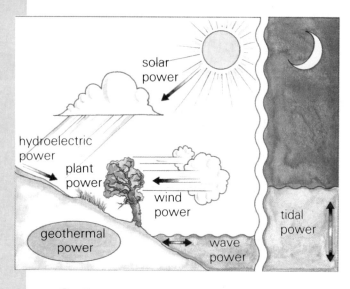

What's the alternative?

With fossil fuels running out, one day we will have to rely on other sources of energy. It may seem a long way off, but if we start using other sources of energy *now*, the remaining fossil fuels will be used less quickly. The other sources of energy may be able to fill the role of a fossil fuel as an *energy* source. But most of them will not be able to provide a ready supply of *chemicals* to make for plastics and other materials. This is why we must use our remaining fossil fuels wisely.

Nuclear power is one option, but what other sources of energy are available in the world around us?

Solar energy

Vast amounts of energy pour down onto the Earth from the Sun every day – a staggering 15 000 times as much as our technological society uses! The problem is, of course, that it is spread out over the entire 'daylight' face of the globe. It also tends to be at a peak where it is least needed – in the desert and at sea. Even so, it can be the equivalent of a 1 bar electric fire on every square metre of the surface. No wonder too much sun can burn!

How can we tap into all this 'free' energy? Many things use **solar cells** which produce electricity directly from sunlight. Examples are solar powered calculators and most types of spacecraft. Solar cells are expensive and, of course, are not very efficient if it's cloudy!

Solar furnaces use mirrors to concentrate the sunlight onto one spot. This can produce temperatures of up to 4000°C, which can be used to drive a generating plant, or directly as a heat source for industry.

Solar panels

A 'gentler' way of using solar energy involves **solar panels** to heat our homes. These use sunlight to heat water in long pipes on the roof. These are painted black to absorb the energy (see page 16).

Even in cloudy Britain, this method could keep a house warm (and even provide hot water) for most of the year. In midwinter, it would need to be supplemented with other forms of heating, but it would still keep the fuel bills down!

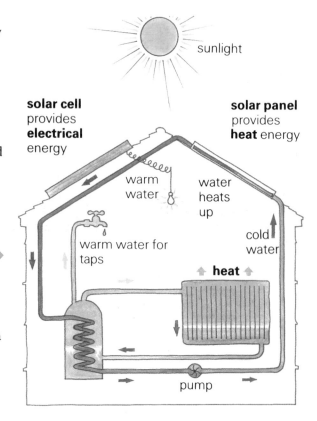

Geothermal energy

Another possible source of energy is the Earth itself! As you go deeper in the crust of the Earth, so the temperature rises, making life hot and sticky for deep miners. Now we have learned how to tap this **geothermal** energy. Water is pumped down to the hot rocks through boreholes, and there it boils. The steam produced is then collected and used to drive turbines and dynamos and so generate electricity. In some places, pipes are laid over cooling hot rocks near volcanoes. Water passed through the pipes gets very hot. It is pumped to nearby towns – providing free hot water!

Plant power!

Plants absorb energy from sunlight and lock it up in chemicals. Scientists in the USA are developing a type of cactus that produces an oily sap which can be refined like crude oil. In Brazil, oil is scarce but sugar cane grows in abundance. The sugar is fermented to make dilute alcohol. This is concentrated by distillation to give industrial alcohol. This is then used in cars as **'gasohol'**, instead of petrol!

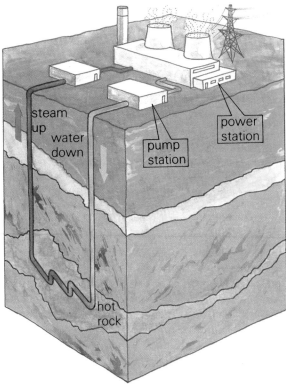

In Mexico, New Zealand, Italy and Iceland geothermal power stations like this are in use.

Using the weather

A large proportion of the solar energy heats up the air, causing it to move around as strong winds. The energy in wind can be seen by the scale of destruction left by a hurricane. The **wind** has also been used for centuries to grind corn and to pump water. Modern windmills use propellor-like blades which drive dynamos and so generate electricity. The weather can also provide energy from rain. The rain water forms rivers that can be trapped by dams. The rivers' potential energy is used to drive **hydroelectric** generators.

Energy from the sea

There are two ways of getting energy from the movement of the sea. **Wave power** uses the rocking motion of the waves to power dynamos. **Tidal power** involves trapping the high tide. The water is then made to flow back to the sea through turbines – which generate electricity.

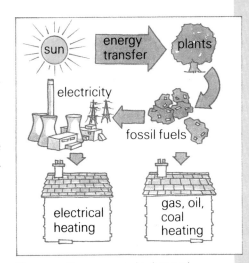

The more times energy is changed from one form to another, the more energy is wasted.

1. List *five* alternatives to fossil fuels. Include *one* that provides a useful chemical.

2. Why are solar cells not always a 'practical solution'?

3. How does a solar furnace work?

4. How can the weather be a source of energy?

5. Why is it more efficient to use fossil fuels to supply heat *directly* rather than using electricity?

14 Nuclear energy

Radioactive decay

Matter is the 'stuff' from which everything is made. Normally, matter and energy are quite separate and distinct – but this is not always the case. The smallest stable particles of matter are called **atoms**. In the case of radioactive material such as **uranium**, the atoms are unstable and can break down – **radioactive decay**. When this happens, a tiny fraction of the matter turns into energy – *a lot of energy*!

The famous scientist Einstein, showed just how much energy with his equation, $E = mc^2$. E is the *energy* released by a *mass m* in a nuclear reaction; c is the speed of light. As the speed of light is very high (300 million metres per second), the amount of energy that can be produced in this way is enormous. 1 unit of matter, if totally converted, will produce 90 000 000 000 000 000 units of energy! This breakdown of large, unstable atoms is called **nuclear fission.**

The international symbol for a radiation hazard.

Nuclear reactors

In a nuclear reactor, unstable 'nuclear fuels' (uranium and plutonium) are allowed to break down under very controlled conditions. The energy produced is used to boil water, make steam, turn a turbine and drive a generator to make electricity in the usual way. About 10% of British electricity is produced in this way – at slightly below the average cost.

Britain has had nuclear reactors in service for 25 years now. The early types needed a special kind of uranium which had to be separated from the 'raw' fuel. The rest of the uranium was then stockpiled. But nowadays modern reactors can use any uranium. By using the old stockpile, Britain already has enough nuclear fuel to produce five times as much energy as all of our North Sea oil!

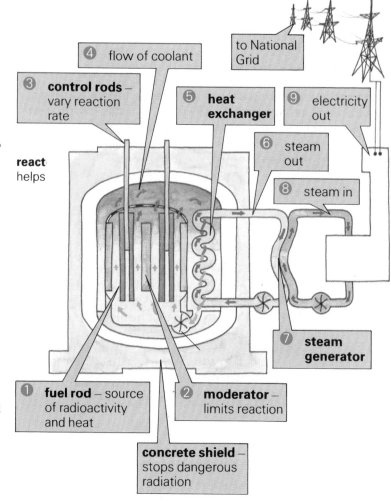

④ flow of coolant

to National Grid

③ **control rods** – vary reaction rate

⑤ **heat exchanger**

⑨ electricity out

⑥ steam out

⑧ steam in

react helps

⑦ **steam generator**

① **fuel rod** – source of radioactivity and heat

② **moderator** – limits reaction

concrete shield – stops dangerous radiation

Nuclear problems

So why worry about fossil fuels if we have nuclear energy? Well, there are many reasons. One is that this same nuclear reaction is responsible for the horrors of nuclear weapons, such as that which destroyed Hiroshima. Countries using nuclear power stations might also learn to make **nuclear weapons** of their own, and the super-powers already have more than enough to destroy the planet – fifty times over!

Also, many people are worried about the nuclear plants themselves. Nuclear reactors produce powerful **radiation** which can kill in large doses. At lower levels, this radiation can also cause cancer and other problems. Because of this, the safety precautions are *very* thorough – much better than in a traditional plant. But human or mechanical error can never be entirely ruled out. There have been **radiation leaks** at nuclear plants all over the world. In the worst accident so far, a serious fire at the Chernobyl plant in Russia caused a very large leak of radioactive material.

The radiation energy from the atomic explosion can cause death and destruction. A nuclear power plant can control this energy to generate electricity.

Nuclear waste

Perhaps more worrying is the fact that nuclear reactors produce lots of radioactive waste. Some of this can be useful if it is reprocessed to make new fuel. But much of it has to be disposed of – and safely. Unfortunately, some radioactive wastes can take thousands of years to become safe, so what do we do with it? Bury it deep in mines? Dump it in the sea? Fire it into space? All of these methods have been investigated at various times.

Clean fusion

In the sun, a different type of nuclear reaction takes place. Small, simple atoms (hydrogen) are being *fused* into larger atoms (helium). This type of **nuclear fusion** is potentially a major step forward for nuclear power. Neither the starting material nor the waste is radioactive! Unfortunately, this reaction needs an enormous 'kick-start' of energy and scientists have not yet mastered this reaction. But work is in progress to harness this vast clean energy for the benefit of everyone. Perhaps nuclear fusion power will be the answer for the future? The problems of our waste-producing 'fission' reactors could be forgotten within a few decades – if we can survive that long...

1   What is unusual about the atoms in radioactive materials?

2   **a**   What happens to the 'lost matter' in nuclear reactions?
     b   Why is so much energy produced?

3   List the problems caused by using nuclear fuels.

4   **a**   What happens in a **fusion** reaction?
     b   Why is it safer than a **fission** reaction?

15 *The nuclear debate*

A tricky question

The nuclear debate has no easy answers. It is related to how we use energy now – and how we plan to use it in the future. The important thing is to understand exactly what both sides are talking about. . .

WE NEED IT!
Fossil fuels will run out. 'Alternative' energy sources are unproven on a large scale. We have large amounts of nuclear fuels already, and we know that it can provide all the energy we need. Once fusion is perfected, we will have limitless energy at our disposal!

STRICT LAWS
The laws are very strict about the levels of radiation allowable in nuclear plants. There is often more radiation in places such as Dartmoor or Aberdeen, which are built on granite.

DEMAND IS INCREASING
More and more energy is being used. People want a more comfortable lifestyle.

IT'S CHEAP
Nuclear reactors in Britain produce electricity more cheaply than 'traditional' power stations.

IT IS SAFE
Even including Chernobyl, there have been fewer accidents and injuries to workers in nuclear plants than in 'traditional' power stations. Look how dangerous coal mining is by comparison! What about the miners killed by accidents and by lung disease? The chance of a major accident at a nuclear power plant in Britain is tiny. Whenever problems have arisen, the built-in safety systems have always worked. Chernobyl was the results of a whole series of 'human errors' that could never have happened here. In fact, Chernobyl has so highlighted the dangers that it will probably never happen again anywhere in the world.

ITS ALL UNDER CONTROL
If all the electricity used by one person in their entire life was generated using nuclear fuels, the total amount of waste fuel would be about the size of a cricket ball! From a coal-fired plant, there would be tonnes of toxic chemical waste to dispose of – not to mention the nasty waste gases and the 'acid rain' they produce.

TERRORISTS COULD USE ANYTHING
A bucket of cyanide from the local factory thrown into the reservoir could kill thousands, too! Unfortunately, terrorists could use almost anything if they wanted to. It's something we have to live with, and try and guard against.

Organise a 'nuclear debate' in your class. Each side should prepare its case in advance. Use newspaper stories to support your ideas.

WE DON'T NEED IT!

The 'alternative' energy sources have not had as much money spent on their development as the nuclear reactors. If we conserve our fossil fuels, there will be plenty of time to perfect the new sources. And they do no harm to the environment. What's more, they will last forever – and are free!

DANGEROUS RAYS!

Nasty rays come from radioactive materials like nuclear fuel and waste. These can cause cancer and other long-term problems.

CUT DEMAND!

It's easy, just get people to insulate their homes. That would reduce demand.

NO IT'S NOT

The latest coal-fired power stations will be cheaper – and we've still got lots of coal left. Rivers, wind and tides can provide cheap *safe* power too!

IT IS DANGEROUS!

However good the system, there is always the possibility of human error, as Chernobyl showed only too clearly. It may not have gone up like an atomic bomb, but it spewed its radioactive waste into the atmosphere. It caused untold damage to the local environment. It also spread with the winds across frontiers and seas. It fell with the rain on Welsh hills, contaminating the sheep and making their meat inedible for many months. And who knows what the long-term effects will be? How many will die untimely deaths of cancer? Will the lives of children yet unborn be affected? The risks are just too great to take.

DANGEROUS WASTE!

The waste from nuclear reactors remains dangerous for hundreds of years or more. Storage problems are bad enough now, but if we went over to nuclear fuels altogether we would be buried in nuclear waste. There is much more than just waste fuel – there's disused equipment, tonnes upon tonnes of it, all radioactive. How could we leave such a menace to our children and our childrens' children?

TERRORISTS COULD USE IT

Nuclear waste contains plutonium. This is also used to make atomic bombs! What is there to stop a terrorist group getting hold of this and making a bomb of their own? Or spreading it around the cities to make them uninhabitable?

Index

Photo acknowledgements

The references indicate page numbers and, where appropriate, the photo sequence.

Barnaby's (M P Brown) 19/2, (Malcolm Pendrill) 20; British coal 22; J Allan Cash, 1, 4/1, 6/1, 23; Sally & Richard Greenhill 4/2, 6/2; GeoScience Features 24; Trevor J Hill 2, 5, 7, 12, 19/1; Frank Lane Agency 16; Rex Features 21; North Scotland Hydroelectric Board 9; Science Photo Library (Alex Bartel) 13; US Navy 29; Sporting Pictures 16; Zeithoper Photoreport 21

Cover photo: Science Photo Library

MODULAR SCIENCE
for GCSE

MODULE *Materials*

Spread

*Different **materials** have different properties. They behave differently under certain physical and chemical conditions. These differences help us to use and develop materials for particular purposes. This module will help you understand more about the nature of materials so that you can recognise, understand their properties and classify them.*

*Relevant National Curriculum
Attainment Target: 3*

1 Making use of materials

Everybody does it!

Humans are different to all the other animals in many, many ways. One way is our ability to make use of a wide variety of materials. Even our Stone Age ancestors used lots of different materials – although they mainly used only natural materials that they could find all around them.

Shelters were originally in caves in the rocks.

Plant juices were used to paint on walls.

The skin or fur of animals was used for clothing.

Bone and wood were strapped together with leather to make spears.

Flint was used to make other tools such as spears and axes.

Simple stone tools made from large pebbles were used to cut meat.

There were not too many people around at the time, and they used only a few materials. Most of these materials came readily to hand. If only things were so simple now. . .

Everyday materials – everywhere!

To-day we still use natural materials, such as wood, but many of the materials that you use everyday are made by us. These 'man-made' or synthetic materials, such as plastic, have to be made in a particular way from natural materials. One advantage of synthetic materials is that they can be made to suit a particular use. Look at the picture below and try to think of reasons why we use the different materials shown.

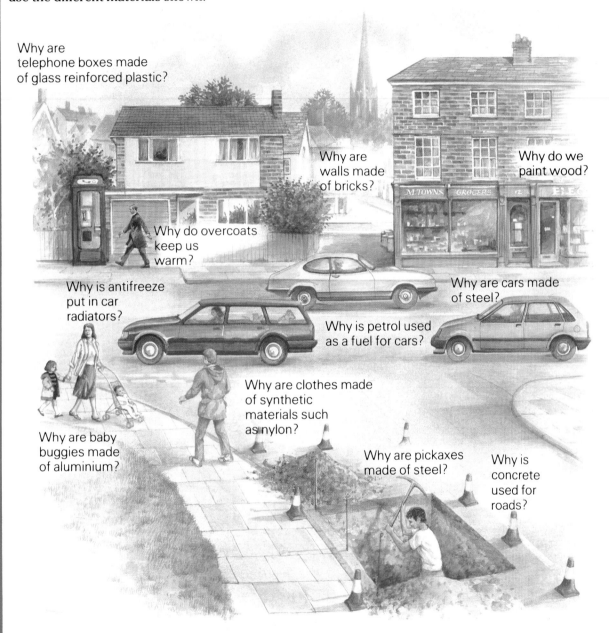

Why are telephone boxes made of glass reinforced plastic?

Why are walls made of bricks?

Why do we paint wood?

Why do overcoats keep us warm?

Why is antifreeze put in car radiators?

Why are cars made of steel?

Why is petrol used as a fuel for cars?

Why are clothes made of synthetic materials such as nylon?

Why are baby buggies made of aluminium?

Why are pickaxes made of steel?

Why is concrete used for roads?

To-day there are many more people using a lot more materials with many different properties. These properties make the materials very useful. But exactly what *are* the properties of materials? How are materials made? What will happen if we use up all the materials?

To find out more, read on ▶

2 Shaping up

Do shapes last?

You have to apply a force in order to shape materials. This force can be such things as a pull or a stretch, a push or a squeeze. If you stretch a rubber balloon by blowing it up, it returns to its original shape when the air is let out. It is said to be **elastic**. Other materials such as pottery clay take on new shapes. These materials are said to be **plastic**.

Clay can be moulded to stay in a new shape.

Let go and the balloon will return to its original shape!

Stretching . . .

Look at the graph. What does it show you about the stretchiness of polythene and nylon? The stretchiness of materials depends not only on the *type* of material but also its *thickness*. What does the graph show you about the change in length of the polythene as it becomes thicker? As the thickness of a material increases, it becomes harder to stretch.

. . . to the limit

Look at the graph. What does it show you about how the length of an elastic material increases as you increase the pull? When a material is elastic, if you double the pull you double the increase in length and so on. However, as the pull increases, the material takes on a new shape. It no longer returns to its original shape. Increasing the pull even more makes the material go more out of shape and eventually it breaks.

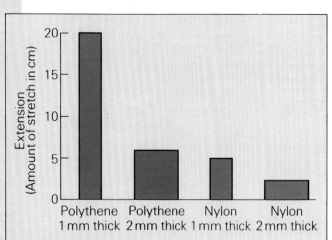

Materials will stretch only so far before they take on a permanent new shape.

The shape of things

When a material no longer returns to its original shape, it has been permanently stretched. This permanent stretching is called **plastic deformation.** Materials which are capable of large plastic deformations can be shaped more easily. They are said to be **ductile**. Some plastics are ductile so they can be easily shaped into useful objects for the home.

The materials used to make these things were easy to shape – they are called 'plastics'.

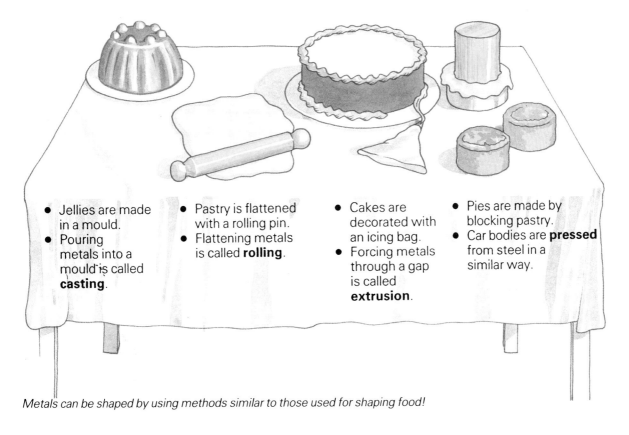

- Jellies are made in a mould.
- Pouring metals into a mould is called **casting**.

- Pastry is flattened with a rolling pin.
- Flattening metals is called **rolling**.

- Cakes are decorated with an icing bag.
- Forcing metals through a gap is called **extrusion**.

- Pies are made by blocking pastry.
- Car bodies are **pressed** from steel in a similar way.

Metals can be shaped by using methods similar to those used for shaping food!

1 Give one example, in each case, of an elastic and plastic material.

2 What is the difference between an elastic and plastic material?

3 State three things which affect the stretchiness of materials.

4 Why do thin woollen jumpers lose their shape more easily than thick ones?

5 Look at the bottom graph opposite.
   a What is the largest pull, in newtons, the material can be given and still remain elastic?
   b What is the smallest pull, in newtons, the material can be given to take on a new shape?

6 Metals are ductile – they can be easily stretched into new shapes. Give two examples of shaping metals, using this property.

3 Look and feel

Looks are Important

The different appearance of materials can be put to good use.

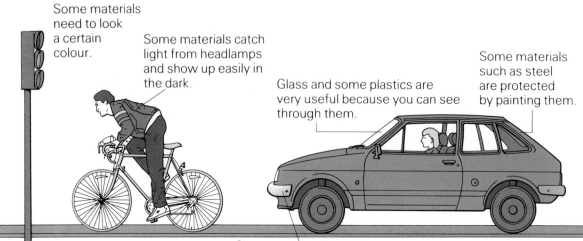

Some materials need to look a certain colour.

Some materials catch light from headlamps and show up easily in the dark.

Glass and some plastics are very useful because you can see through them.

Some materials such as steel are protected by painting them.

Chrome protects metals which are scratched too often to use paint.

Looking the same

All materials are made up of tiny particles. The appearance of a material depends on the type of particle it is made from and the way these are arranged. Metals, for example, are made up of particles called **atoms** arranged in a similar way so that most metals look very similar. Different plastics, such as polythene and polypropylene which are used in packaging food, are difficult to tell apart because they have the same atoms arranged in a very similar way.

A rough diamond looks like a piece of glass because they have a similar arrangement of particles.

Looking different

Some materials can be made to look different by adding other materials. Glass and plastic, for example, have other materials added to give them colour. Some materials have their appearance altered by coating their surface. Wood can be painted to make it a different colour or varnished to make it look shiny. Metals, such as iron, have a coating of another metal, for example chromium, put on them by a process known as **electroplating.**

Which materials in this picture have had their appearance changed?

Feeling right

The 'feel' of a material is called its **texture**. Some materials are made to have a smooth texture, others are made with a rough texture. It all depends on what they are to be used for . . .

Some clothes such as wool have a soft texture.

Sharp metals may have to be smoothed down.

Plastics feel smooth.

Abrasives such as 'wet and dry' must feel rough.

Tyres must feel rough if they are to get a good grip on a road surface.

The large crystals of zinc make zinc-coated metals feel rough.

Feeling different

The texture also depends on the type of particle in a material and the way they are arranged. Some materials have a regular arrangement of particles called a **crystal**. These crystals can join up to form grains of different sizes. The texture depends on the size and hardness of the grains. If the grains are large and hard the material feels rough. **Abrasives**, such as sandpaper, are used to make the grains on the surface of a material, smaller. Some materials, such as wool and plastics are not made of crystals – they have a different structure.

1 What is the name given to a material you can see through?

2 Why do some plastics have a similar appearance?

3 Name four articles which are often chromium plated.

4 If you wanted to coat a nickel wedding ring with silver what process would you use?

5 Why are smooth tyres on cars dangerous?

6 **a** Why does the surface of a metal normally feel rough?
b What does an abrasive do to the surface?

4 Conductors and insulators

Energy on the move

Different materials can be used to control the movement of energy...

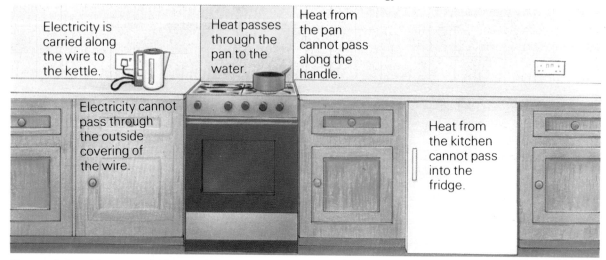

Electricity is carried along the wire to the kettle.

Heat passes through the pan to the water.

Heat from the pan cannot pass along the handle.

Electricity cannot pass through the outside covering of the wire.

Heat from the kitchen cannot pass into the fridge.

Heat and electricity are useful forms of energy – but to make full use of them, you have to control their movement.

Conductors and insulators

Materials which allow energy to pass along them easily are called **conductors**. Those which do not are called **insulators.** Metals such as silver and copper, are good conductors of heat and electricity. Materials like wood, rubber and plastics are all insulators. They do not allow energy to pass along them as easily as conductors.

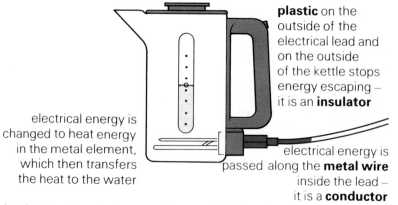

electrical energy is changed to heat energy in the metal element, which then transfers the heat to the water

plastic on the outside of the electrical lead and on the outside of the kettle stops energy escaping – it is an **insulator**

electrical energy is passed along the **metal wire** inside the lead – it is a **conductor**

Insulators and conductors are often used side by side.

Spoilt for choice

All metals are conductors but some are better conductors than others. Look at the picture. Along which metal has the heat travelled furthest in one minute? Silver is a better conductor than either iron or copper but it is very expensive ... so it is not a good choice for everyday use.

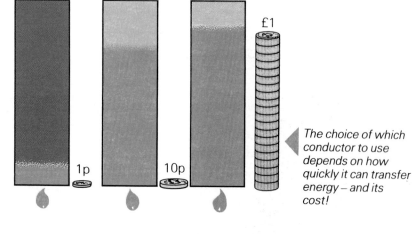

IRON   COPPER   SILVER

£1

1p   10p

The choice of which conductor to use depends on how quickly it can transfer energy – and its cost!

Saving heat

Insulators are useful for stopping things getting too hot. They stop heat energy from escaping. Metal saucepans have plastic or wooden handles to stop them from burning your hands. Air is a good heat insulator, so anything that traps air is also a good insulator. This is why glass fibre is used for loft insulation. It costs a lot to make heat energy, so if you let heat escape, you are wasting money . . . it is worth insulating your home against this waste.

Clothes and fur keep us and animals warm by trapping air in layers. This air keeps the heat in.

This electrical equipment is well insulated by plastic coated wire and plastic drill casing. Even the ear 'mufflers' insulate against sound energy!

Playing safe

Electricity, carrying a lot of energy, can harm or even kill you. To stop this happening all electrical plugs, sockets and leads are made with thick plastic covers. Tools and other electrical appliances, such as hairdriers, have insulated rubber or plastic handles. Some insulators can become conductors, if they are carrying a lot of energy. Water, for example, will conduct electricity from the mains supply. This is why electrical appliances should never be used near a bath full of water.

1 Name two forms of energy.

2 Name three materials which are good insulators.

3 Look at the metal rods opposite. If you held each metal at the top end, which metal would feel warm first?

4 Why are metals conductors?

5 **a** Animals have fur or feathers to keep warm. What clothes do you wear to keep warm?
   b Explain how these clothes keep you warm.

6 Why do TVs have warning signs at the back of them?

5 Heavyweights and lightweights

A dense situation

You can compare the heaviness of two materials by putting them at each end of a see-saw. You can also compare the **density** of two materials in this way. This is a measure of how much 'stuff' of a material is packed into a particular volume of it. Look at these pictures of two different materials on a see-saw . . .

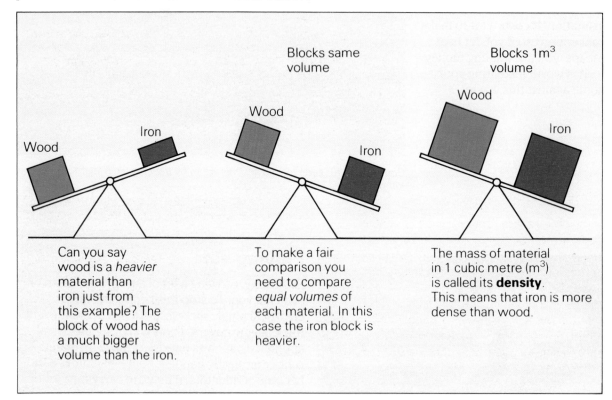

Blocks same volume

Blocks 1m³ volume

Can you say wood is a *heavier* material than iron just from this example? The block of wood has a much bigger volume than the iron.

To make a fair comparison you need to compare *equal volumes* of each material. In this case the iron block is heavier.

The mass of material in 1 cubic metre (m³) is called its **density**. This means that iron is more dense than wood.

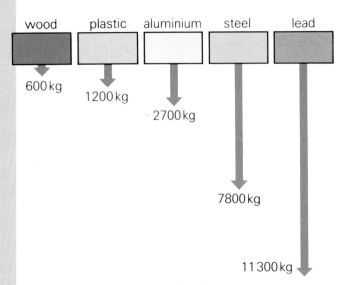

wood — 600 kg
plastic — 1200 kg
aluminium — 2700 kg
steel — 7800 kg
lead — 11 300 kg

Some materials, such as lead, are more tightly packed than others.

What makes materials 'heavy'?

Some materials, such as metals, are neatly packed and close, together, like biscuits in a packet. Other materials, such as plastics, are not so neatly packed and have large gaps of air between them. Look at the diagram which shows the masses of one cubic metre (m³) of different materials. What does it show you about how the type of packing of the materials affects their density?

'Light' is right

'Lighter', or less dense, materials need less energy to lift or carry them. Bricks are about three times more dense than wooden planks. A person working on a building site, would use three times more energy lifting a hodful of bricks than lifting wooden beams of the same volume. . . but maybe a handful of bricks is slightly easier to handle!

Brick is more dense than wood . . . a hodful of bricks is quite a heavyweight compared to a plank of wood!

Changing density

Some objects that are not dense enough can be made denser by filling up the air gaps with denser materials. The steel hull of a submarine or the hollow plastic base of a sunshade can be made denser by replacing the air with water. Materials that need to be made less dense (lighter, but with the same volume), can have air bubbled into them. For example, polystyrene has air blown into it to make much lighter **expanded polystyrene.**

A lightweight shade can get blown over. Fill the base with water and it becomes denser, and so heavier and more stable.

'Heavy' hits back

It might seem that 'heavy', dense materials have little use. However, walk around any town or glance around the school or home and you will see examples of objects such as litter bins, paper weights and laboratory stands that are heavy enough to stay in one place but not so heavy they cannot be lifted. And some things, such as statues and paving slabs, shouldn't move at all!

1 How many times more dense than plastic is wood?

2 Explain why lead is more dense than plastic.

3 Why are aeroplanes made of aluminium and not steel?

4 A man, lifting bricks, used '15 packets of cornflakes' worth of energy. How much would have been used lifting the same amount of wood?

5 Explain why wet clothes are heavier than dry.

6 Why is packaging material often made of expanded polystyrene?

6 Strength

What is strength?

A strong material is one which is difficult to break when you apply a **force**. This force can be a pull such as a climber would use to test a climbing rope. It can also be a squeeze or a crushing blow such as a builder might use on stone slabs when making crazy paving. A material which is difficult to break by pulling is said to have good **tensile strength**. One which is difficult to break by crushing is said to have good **compressive strength**.

This climber is glad that a thick nylon rope has good tensile strength.

This job is hard work because concrete has good compressive strength.

Strong stuff

Some materials are used because they have good compressive strength. A good example is a brick which has to be able to withstand the squashing of all the other bricks above it. It is about 20 times more difficult to squash a brick than to stretch it.

The usefulness of ropes, lines and chains depends on their tensile strength. Look at the bar chart. What does it show you about the increasing use of synthetic fibres such as nylon for ropes instead of natural ones such as manilla or sisal?

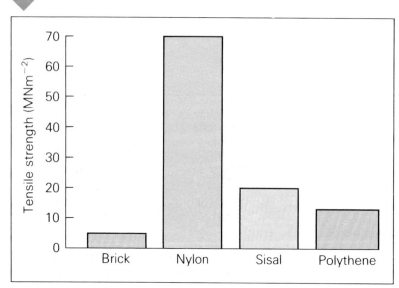

One brick can support the weight of 40 000 others before it will be crushed.

Bar chart: Tensile strength (MNm^{-2})

Material	Tensile strength (MNm^{-2})
Brick	~5
Nylon	70
Sisal	~20
Polythene	~12

Strength and area

The tensile strength of a material depends on its cross-sectional area. Look at the diagram below. If the area of the material is 4 times larger, the force required to break it needs to be four times as big. The compressive strength can be increased in the same way.

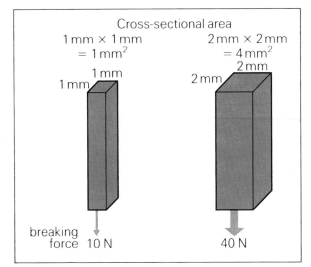

By increasing the thickness four times, a material will become four times stronger.

Very thin spider's webs still have great tensile strength. If 200 times thicker, their silk would support a car!

Bending

A material which is being pulled, is made longer and it is said to be under **tension**. A material which is being squashed, is made shorter, and it is said to be under **compression**. If the opposite sides of a material are being squashed and stretched at the same time, it is being **bent**. If a material is easy to bend it is **flexible** and it has good compressive and tensile strength.

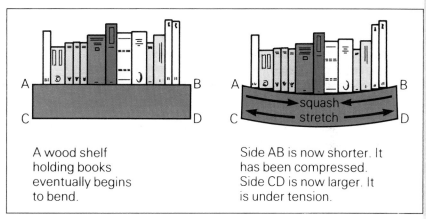

A wood shelf holding books eventually begins to bend.

Side AB is now shorter. It has been compressed. Side CD is now larger. It is under tension.

If a shelf is to resist bending, the material must have a high tensile strength **and** a high compressive strength.

1. Give one example of a material which has good **a** compressive strength, **b** tensile strength.

2. Look at the bar chart.
   a What is the compressive strength of a brick if it is 20 times greater than its tensile strength?
   b What is the tensile strength of nylon?
   c Why do climbers prefer nylon ropes to natural fibres such as sisal?

3. Look at figure at the top left of this page. What would be the breaking force if the cross-sectional area were 100 mm²?

4. The tensile strength of steel is about 2100 Nm² and that of nylon about 70 Nm². If a steel wire had a cross-sectional area of 10 mm², what would the area of nylon rope need to be in order to have the same tensile strength?

5. Concrete has good compressive but poor tensile strength. Why is it not flexible?

7 Composite materials

Tough and brittle

Some useful materials such as glass and concrete are **brittle**. A brittle material usually cracks under a force and any more energy being used to break it passes along the crack making it bigger.

Tough materials such as steel used for car bodies are not as easy to break. If a force is applied to a tough material (such as a car tyre), it absorbs energy from the force. A tough material often absorbs energy by changing shape slightly – but it will not break.

Although tough materials and brittle materials have separate uses, sometimes they may be combined to make more useful materials.

Concrete is brittle; under large forces it will crack rather than gradually change its shape.

Making materials tougher

Materials can be made tougher if you can stop them cracking. In order to do this, brittle materials such as plaster and some plastics are combined with a material made of fibre such as glass fibre or paper. The energy used which would normally break the brittle material is passed along the fibre instead. This principle is used to make glass reinforced plastic (GRP) which contains glass fibre in a brittle plastic resin. Such materials are called **composite** materials. ▼

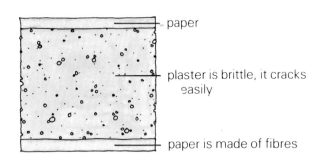

paper

plaster is brittle, it cracks easily

paper is made of fibres

Plasterboard is made by coating a plaster core with paper fibres. The paper helps to stop the plaster from cracking.

CONCRETE BRIDGE

The bottom section of the bridge is being stretched by the weight of the cars passing over it. Concrete is brittle when it is stretched and can crack.

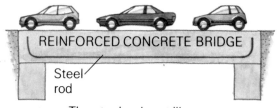

REINFORCED CONCRETE BRIDGE

Steel rod

The steel rods act like fibres. Energy being used to try and crack the concrete is passed along the steel rods instead.

Bridges of only concrete crack under the weight of cars. Steel rods prevent the cracks from forming.

Making materials stronger

Some materials, such as wood, are strong in certain directions. Plywood consists of layers of wood bonded together. In one layer the grains run *across* the wood, in the next layer the grains run *along* the wood. Look at the picture. What does it show you about how more strength can be given to the wood by making it plywood?

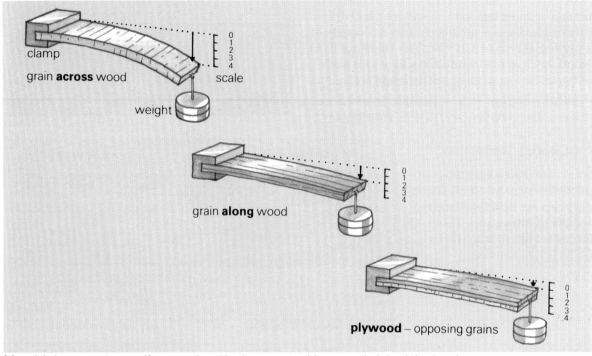

Materials become stronger if arranged so that they are not able to use their 'grain' to bend.

Materials can also be made stronger by altering their shape. Large thin sheets of plastic are too bendy to use as roofing material. Cardboard boxes, used in packaging, also need to be stiff to protect their contents. One way of improving the stiffness of materials is to alter its shape by **corrugating**.

Materials break when forces act on a weak point. Corrugation helps to spread these forces around, making the material stronger. Folded newspaper can support a heavy weight of water!

---

1 Name one brittle and one tough material.

2 What is the difference between a brittle and a tough material?

3 Explain why horsehair used to be added to plaster.

4 Look at the diagram of wood, above.
   a Is wood stronger when weights are placed along or across the grain?
   b In what direction do you think wood grain should run in a beam supporting a roof?

5 Name two advantages of using corrugated cardboard instead of cardboard sheets for packaging.

8 Hard and hardwearing

What is hardness?

A **hard** material is one which is difficult to scratch or dent. It is a property which only solid materials have. All solids are hard compared to liquids or gases but some solids are harder than others. Hardness is not necessarily a property of a particular type of material since there are hard woods such as mahogany and soft woods such as balsa. Similarly, there are hard and soft metals and plastics.

Synthetic diamonds are extremely hard ▶

Packing them in!

Solids are made of particles packed closely together. These particles are held together by **forces of attraction.** These forces act like mortar which holds bricks together.

Most hard materials have very closely packed particles held together by strong forces. Soft materials are usually less closely packed and held only weakly. ▶

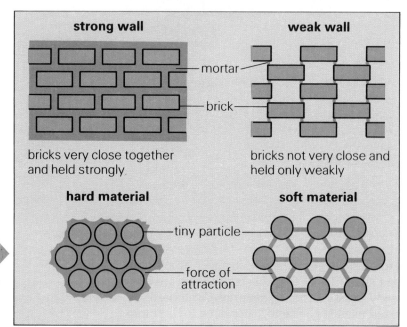

strong wall

bricks very close together and held strongly

weak wall

— mortar

— brick

bricks not very close and held only weakly

hard material

— tiny particle —

— force of attraction

soft material

The hard stuff

Tungsten carbide is a very hard metal alloy and is used to drill through steel or concrete. Metal cutters made of steel can slice through tin. The rubbing action of sandpaper cuts into wood, producing a smooth finish. Look at the table. What does it show you about how the hardness of the materials is related to their use?

Hardness index	Material
10	Diamond
9·7	Silicon carbide
8·5	Tungsten carbide drill
7→5	Steel
7·0	Sand
5·5	Glass
5·5	Nickel
5→4	Concrete
1·5	Tin
3→1	Wood

The harder a material, the higher its number in the hardness index.

Hardwearing

Materials can wear out from the constant rubbing action of other materials. Rubber bicycle brakes wear out and need replacing because they are worn out by the hard metal rims of the bicycle wheel. Materials that are hard, such as diamond, are not worn out by softer materials so they are **hardwearing.** Natural materials such as cotton from plants, and wool from animals, are not hardwearing. This is because in their natural state, even if they wear away, they can be replaced by the growth of new material.

If a sheep's coat needs replacing, new wool grows. If the clippers wear out, they have to be sharpened.

A longer life

Materials can be arranged so that they resist the rubbing action of other materials better. One way of doing this is to **pack** the material more tightly, for example, using a steam roller to make a road more hardwearing. Or in the case of a fibre, such as cotton, it can be woven more closely together.

Materials can also be **mixed** with other materials that are more hardwearing. Woolen jumpers often contain an artificial fibre (such as nylon) which is more hardwearing. This helps these jumpers to last through more wear and washing.

Made at first as tough clothes for working in, the material for hardwearing jeans is made by weaving tightly packed thick cotton fibres.

1 Name one hard and one soft wood.

2 Explain why high impact polystyrene is harder than expanded polystyrene.

3 Look at the table on hardness.
   a Name one hard and one soft metal
   b Why is silicon carbide paper used instead of sandpaper to rub down car bodies?
   c Why is diamond used widely in industry as a cutting tool?

4 Why do the elbows of woolen jumpers wear out first?

5 Why does weaving a fibre more closely together make it more hardwearing?

6 Look at the labels on some of your clothes. What artificial fibres have been mixed with natural fibres like cotton and wool? List the combinations you can find

9 Rotten materials

Its rotten!

Materials that rot are being eaten away by **decomposers** such as bacteria and fungi. These are tiny organisms that are all around us. They are so small that you can't see them, and so light they are easily carried by the wind from place to place. When they land on food, they multiply or reproduce at a very quick rate. You can see the rapid growth of fungi as mould on food.

Air raid! Fungi and bacteria from the air grow rapidly once they find material to feed on.

What type of materials rot?

Fungi and bacteria, unlike plants, can't make their own food. They feed on the carbohydrates found in dead material such as paper and wood. They also need **damp** conditions but will eat any dead wood, whether in a forest or part of a house. When the wood is being eaten away, it loses all its strength. This can be a serious problem because wood is used in houses as a support in beams, window frames and floorboards.

A picnic in the woods for decomposers – rotted wood lies all around the base of this dead tree.

Types of rot

Different fungi produce different types of rot but in this country they are divided into two types: wet and dry rot. Wet rot is fairly common but is easily cured. Dry rot is less common but more of a problem – it can lie 'hidden' in the wood and so may reappear long after treatment. Look at the pictures of wet and dry rot. How do you think they get their names?

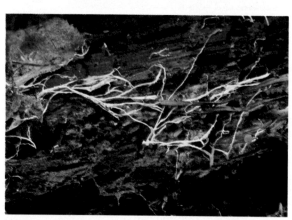

Wet rot – after landing on damp wood, this fungus produces white stalks (hyphae) which spread across the wood.

Dry rot – a tiny fungus which is difficult to control. It can even move along brickwork to attack nearby wood.

Prevention is better than cure

Dampness can enter buildings in a number of ways. This means conditions will then exist for wood to decay. New buildings should be designed using the right materials to prevent the possibility of damp getting in. Existing buildings must be properly maintained to keep damp out. Look at the picture. What does it show you about some of the causes of dampness entering a building? What must be done, do you think, to prevent the dampness?

If the slate and gutter were repaired soon after the ridge tiles blew off, there would have been no other problems.

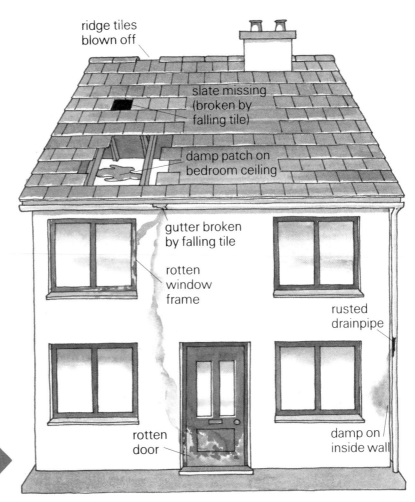

ridge tiles blown off

slate missing (broken by falling tile)

damp patch on bedroom ceiling

gutter broken by falling tile

rotten window frame

rusted drainpipe

rotten door

damp on inside wall

Breaking down, building up

Rotting is nature's way of breaking animal and plant material down so that it can be used again – **recycling** materials. If rotting didn't take place, then essential food for plants would soon run out. Gardeners make use of this process when they build a **compost** heap. However materials such as plastics, which don't rot are used today. Look at the bar chart. What does it show you about the use of plastics and paper compared with thirty years ago?

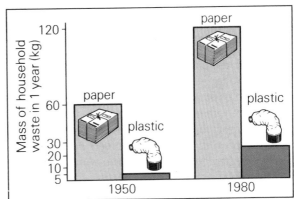

Nowadays we are making even more of a mess!

---

1 Why is it very difficult to kill all fungi?

2 State two conditions needed for fungi to grow and multiply.

3 Why is wood rot a problem and why is dry rot more serious than wet rot?

4 Look at the picture of the house. Identify four ways that dampness could get inside. Suggest possible cures.

5 Look at the bar chart.
  a By how much has the amount of plastics used increased in the last thirty years?
  b Why is 'plastic rubbish' a problem and how might it be solved?

10 *Change of state*

How do materials move?

Have you ever wondered how you can soon smell the gas when you've left the cooker on, but unlit? If you left a tap running, you would not know until much later, when the water flowed under your feet. Can you explain why snow piled up against a door stays in place, even when the door is opened?

These materials behave in different ways because they are in different **states** – one is a **gas**, one a **liquid** and the other a **solid**.

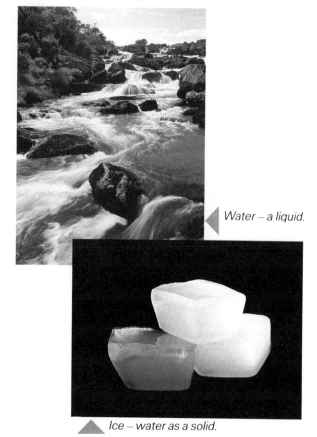

Water – a liquid.

Steam – water as a gas.

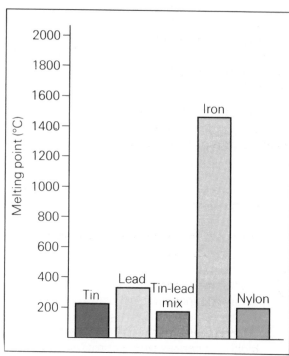

Ice – water as a solid.

Energy for a change

The faster the particles in a material are moving, the more energy it has. When a solid is **heated**, the particles **gain** energy and vibrate more. As they gain more energy, they are able to move much more freely and become liquids. By cooling a liquid, energy is removed, so the particles slow down and become solids again.

Altered states – solids to liquids . . .

The temperature at which a solid changes to a liquid is called its **melting point**. A material with a low melting point, such as nylon, melts more easily than one with a high melting point, such as iron. Materials can be made to melt more easily by adding other substances. Salt is added to icy roads in winter to make the ice melt more easily. Look at the graph. What does it show you about how the melting point of lead and tin can be changed by mixing them together?

Some materials melt more easily than others.

. . . liquids to gases

The temperature at which a liquid changes to a gas is called its **boiling point.** Some liquids, like water, are made up of particles that are very small and light. These particles are free to move about easily, so only a little energy is needed to change them into gases. Such liquids have low boiling points.

Other liquids are made up of large, heavy molecules which need a lot of energy to make them move fast enough to become gases. These liquids have high boiling points, for example, cooking oil boils at 250°C.

All mixed up

Some liquids are made up of mixtures of different particles. Crude oil is an example of such a liquid mixture. Some of the particles are small and light; these particles boil before the heavier ones. By slowly increasing the temperature, first the light particles boil off – these can be cooled and **condensed** (collected as a liquid). After more heating, the heavier particles boil off – these too can be cooled and collected.

In this way, the mixture has been separated by a process called **fractional distillation**.

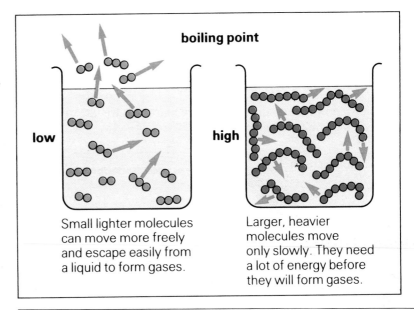

boiling point

low Small lighter molecules can move more freely and escape easily from a liquid to form gases.

high Larger, heavier molecules move only slowly. They need a lot of energy before they will form gases.

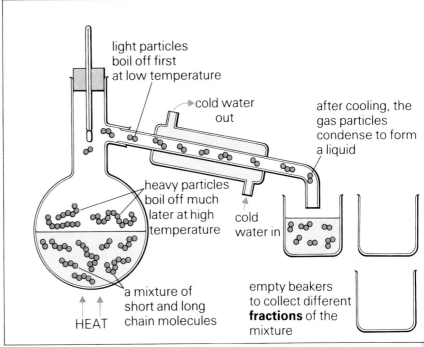

light particles boil off first at low temperature

cold water out

after cooling, the gas particles condense to form a liquid

heavy particles boil off much later at high temperature

cold water in

a mixture of short and long chain molecules

HEAT

empty beakers to collect different **fractions** of the mixture

A typical apparatus for the fractional distillation of a mixture of liquids.

---

1 How does the movement in gases compare to that in liquids?

2 Why does steam turn back into water when it hits a cold window?

3 Look at the bar chart opposite.
   a How does the melting point of the tin–lead mixture compare with that of pure tin and pure lead?
   b Why is tin not used to make the wires of light bulbs which reach 800°C?

4 Why is oil more runny when it is hot than cold?

5 Why is antifreeze added to car radiators in winter?

6 Look at diagram of the boiling mixture.
   a Why is the mixture heated?
   b What is the purpose of the cold water?
   c How does the boiling point of the short molecules compare with that of the long molecules?

11 Crude oil

Where does oil come from?

The oil we now rely on for many of the materials we use today was formed many millions of years ago. . .

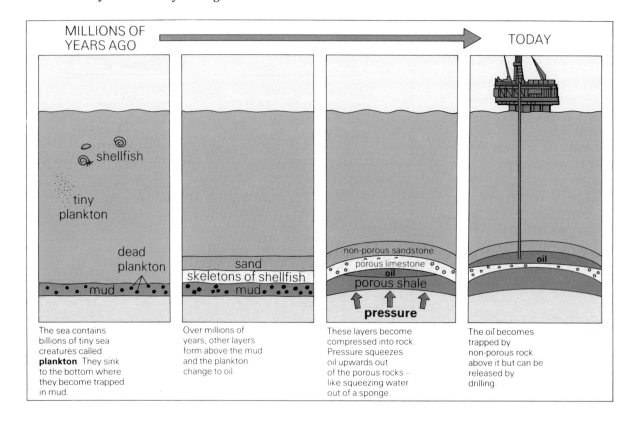

MILLIONS OF YEARS AGO → TODAY

shellfish

tiny plankton

dead plankton

mud

The sea contains billions of tiny sea creatures called **plankton**. They sink to the bottom where they become trapped in mud.

sand
skeletons of shellfish
mud

Over millions of years, other layers form above the mud and the plankton change to oil.

non-porous sandstone
porous limestone
oil
porous shale
pressure

These layers become compressed into rock. Pressure squeezes oil upwards out of the porous rocks – like squeezing water out of a sponge.

oil

The oil becomes trapped by non-porous rock above it but can be released by drilling.

What is oil used for?

Nowadays many materials with useful properties are obtained or made from crude oil like those shown in these pictures . . .

Nylon – a plastic which makes strong ropes, smooth stockings and hardwearing gears.

Plastics – these can be easily shaped and coloured.

Paraffin – burnt to give light and heat.

Solvents – such as nail varnish, and 'white spirit' for dissolving paints.

What is crude oil?

Crude oil is a mixture of compounds called **hydrocarbons**. Hydrocarbons contain particles called *molecules*. These molecules are made up of even smaller particles – *atoms* – of hydrogen and carbon joined together in chains. These molecules have a backbone of carbon atoms. The number of carbon atoms or the chain length is different for each type of hydrocarbon. Molecules with a long chain length are heavier and less runny than those with a short chain length.

Separating the mixture

As you have seen, crude oil is a mixture of many useful substances, all of which have different boiling points. These can be separated out by a process called fractional distillation (see page 53). The oil is heated in a large column called a **fractionating column** where it is separated into the different parts, called **fractions**. This is done on a very large scale in the industrial process of the fractional distillation of oil.

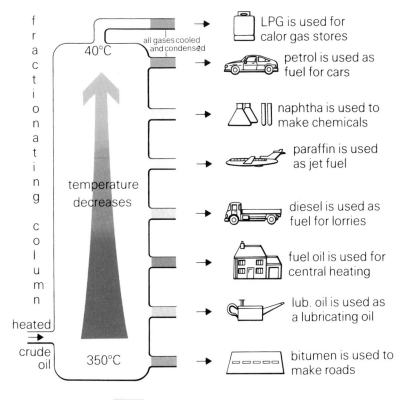

Figure 1. Crude oil is a mixture of many different parts. Each part of the mixture is made up of hydrocarbons with a particular number of carbon atoms.

Figure 2. You can see how useful crude oil is once it is separated into its various fractions.

1. What is oil made from?

2. Look at the pictures of different materials on the opposite page. Which materials are obtained *directly* by fractional distillation of crude oil?

3. Look at Figure 1b above. Put the data shown in the form of a bar chart.

4. Look at Figure 1a. How does it show you that paraffin is a mixture of hydrocarbons and not a pure compound?

5. Look at Figure 1a. How does it show you that petrol is more runny than bitumen?

6. Look at Figures 1 and 2. What do they show you about the boiling point of a hydrocarbon as its chain length increases?

12 *Plastics*

- Tonnes of petrol
- Tonnes of naphtha
- Tonnes of paraffin
- Tonnes of diesel
- Tonnes of fuel oil
- Tonnes of lube oil
- Tonnes of others

Yet more uses of oil

Crude oil can be processed even more to produce 'extra helpings' of the parts that are in great demand. Other products can be made which are used to make **plastics** – materials which you probably use every day, all the time...

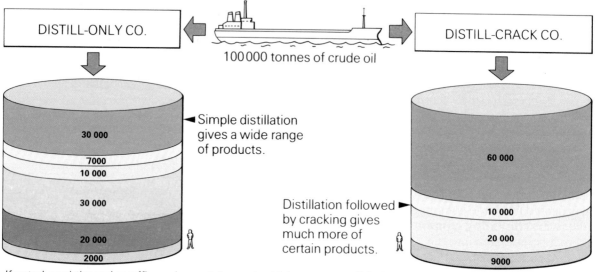

DISTILL-ONLY CO.

100 000 tonnes of crude oil

DISTILL-CRACK CO.

| 30 000 |
| 7000 |
| 10 000 |
| 30 000 |
| 20 000 |
| 2000 |

◄ Simple distillation gives a wide range of products.

Distillation followed ► by cracking gives much more of certain products.

| 60 000 |
| 10 000 |
| 20 000 |
| 9000 |

If petrol, naphtha and paraffin are in great demand, which company will find it easiest to sell its products?

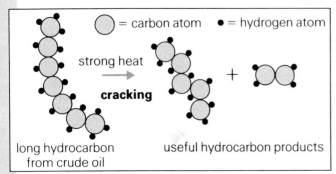

○ = carbon atom   ● = hydrogen atom

strong heat

cracking

long hydrocarbon from crude oil

useful hydrocarbon products

Strong heating causes the carbon chain in a long hydrocarbon to break – producing smaller hydrocarbons.

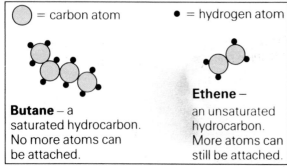

○ = carbon atom   ● = hydrogen atom

Butane – a saturated hydrocarbon. No more atoms can be attached.

Ethene – an unsaturated hydrocarbon. More atoms can still be attached.

Cracking produces saturated and unsaturated compounds.

The fractions are made up of compounds called hydrocarbons (see page 55). **Hydrocarbons** are molecules made up of hydrogen and carbon atoms joined together in a chain. The backbone of the chain consists of carbon atoms. Heating the molecule causes it to vibrate more. Continued heating will vibrate the molecule enough to break the carbon chain. This means that long chain molecules can be shortened. The breaking of the chain is called **cracking**.

When a hydrocarbon molecule is cracked, the number of hydrogen and carbon atoms remain the same but they have been rearranged. One part of the chain may now contain carbon atoms which are surrounded by *four* other atoms. No more atoms can be attached and it is said to be **saturated**.

The other part contains some carbon atoms surrounded by only *three* atoms. More atoms can still be attached to these carbon atoms, and it is said to be **unsaturated**. These **unsaturated** compounds are the useful products.

How are they useful?

Because more atoms can still be attached, the small unsaturated hydrocarbons are more useful than the saturated hydrocarbons. These small molecules, called **monomers**, can be joined together to form plastics or **polymers**. For example, the monomer **ethene** can form the polymer **polyethene** (**polythene**). Polythene can be made with chain lengths of 1000 to 20 000 carbon atoms. This is done by altering the conditions of **polymerisation**. Other polymers can also be made using different monomers. These polymers are often called **plastics** because they can be easily shaped during manufacture.

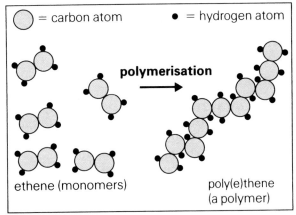

Different forms of plastics have different properties – each property gives rise to different uses.

What are plastics used for?

Today we really do live in a 'plastic' world. . .

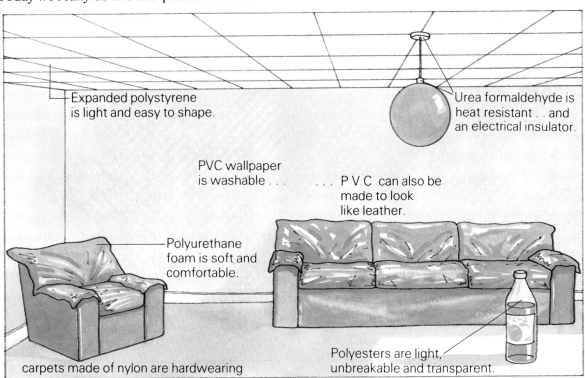

Expanded polystyrene is light and easy to shape.

Urea formaldehyde is heat resistant . . and an electrical insulator.

PVC wallpaper is washable . . .

. . . P V C can also be made to look like leather.

Polyurethane foam is soft and comfortable.

carpets made of nylon are hardwearing

Polyesters are light, unbreakable and transparent.

1. Look at the figure on the opposite page
   a Which fractions are cracked after being distilled?
   b Which fraction was produced in the greatest amount by cracking?

2. Why is heat needed for cracking?

3. What is the difference between a saturated and unsaturated hydrocarbon?

4. Draw the shape of the polymer formed by joining 10 ethene monomers. Explain why the polymer can still increase its chain length.

5. Plastic bottles for fizzy drinks are made of polyesters. What properties does it have which make it ideal for this use?

6. Why do some people think the use of crude oil as a fuel wastes resources?

13 Flammable materials

Burning up!

To burn a material you need *oxygen*, which is present in the air, and a source of *heat*. Materials, such as petrol or natural gas, which burn very easily are said to be **highly flammable**. Materials that don't burn are said to be **non-flammable**, such as most metals. Metals usually just melt when they are heated. Other non-flammable materials, such as limestone, break down into simpler substances.

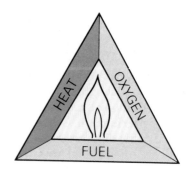

*If materials are to act as **fuels**, they need **heat** and **oxygen**. Remove just one of these and the fire will go out.*

When materials burn . . .

When some materials burn they produce harmful substances. . .

Natural gas produces heat and harmless invisible gases such as carbon dioxide and water.

A lot of heat is produced from a burning sofa. In 3 minutes the temperature of the room can rise by 1000°C.

Invisible poisonous gases, such as carbon monoxide and hydrogen cyanide, are produced.

A lot of carbon in the form of soot or smoke is produced – make breathing very difficult.

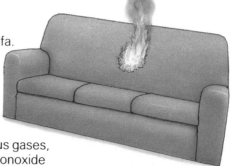

Soft padding used to be made from animal hair but up to now polyurethane foam was used instead. This foam may be cheap, but in a fire it is dangerous.

A controlled fire in the home is fine – an uncontrolled furniture fire can be lethal.

Nowadays, all new furniture sold in Britain has to be fire resistant. This should help to reduce the number of deaths in household fires.

Chips are dangerous!

Don't *try to use water,* **don't** *try to take it outside like this. Cover with a damp towel. Remove the pan from the cooker.* **Don't** *remove the towel until the pan cools.*

Many people have chips at least once a week, yet frying chips is the main cause of fire in the home. Fat or cooking oil are not very flammable substances, but when overheated they give off a blue smoke and can catch fire spontaneously. Alternatively, the oil or fat spills or spits over onto the cooker and catches fire.

A flammable test

Wool, as a carpet material, is now being replaced by artificial fibres such as nylon. One method of comparing how easily they burn is to place a hot metal nut on a carpet for 30 seconds and examine the size of the burn. Look at the results in the picture. What do they show you about the flammability of nylon and wool?

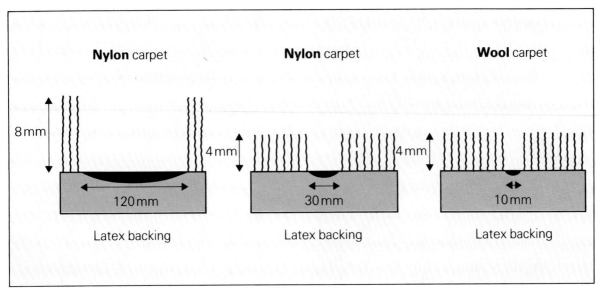

Predict how large the burn mark will be for a 'long pile' wool carpet.

Beating the flames

Some materials, such as asbestos, are very flame resistant and do not catch fire easily. Most materials, however, have to be treated with a flame retardant or flame proofing solution such as **borax** to make them safer. Burns, however, are not only caused by flames but by the heat produced by charred material still glowing when the flame has gone out.

Look at the table. What does it show you about the effect of washing flame proof materials?

	Untreated Cotton	**Cotton treated with borax**	**Cotton treated with borax and washed**
Flame test	Flame spreads immediately	Flame takes 10 seconds to spread	Flame takes 6 seconds to spread
Smoulder test	Charred material glows red for 30 seconds	Charred material glows red for 5 seconds	Charred material glows red for 12 seconds

Flame retardents, such as borax, make materials less flammable.

1. Look at the sign of the fire triangle. Why are the sides labelled heat, oxygen and fuel?

2. Why do petrol stations have 'NO SMOKING' signs?

3. Look at the diagram of the burning sofa.
   a Why are people often not able to escape from these fires?
   b What do you think are the most likely causes of these fires?

4. Look at the carpet burns shown above. What effect does **a** the pile height **b** the type of fibre have on the size of the burn.

5. Why do fire fighters sometimes wear asbestos suits?

6. Why do flameproof materials need to be retreated after washing a few times?

14 Materials – 'tailor-made' for

A car is made of many different materials. Each material has particular properties which make it right for the job. . .

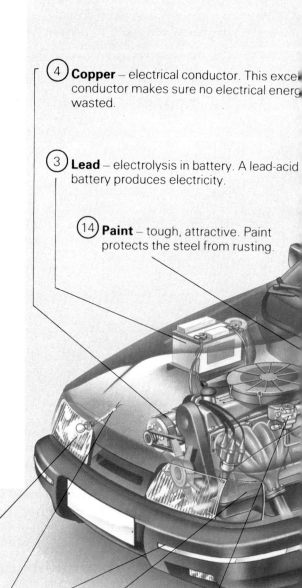

④ **Copper** – electrical conductor. This exce[ ] conductor makes sure no electrical energ[ ] wasted.

③ **Lead** – electrolysis in battery. A lead-acid battery produces electricity.

⑭ **Paint** – tough, attractive. Paint protects the steel from rusting.

① **Glass** – transparent. It lets the light out from the headlamp, but keeps water and dust out.

② **Plastic** (PVC) – electrical insulator. This makes sure the flow of electricity stays inside the wire.

⑮ **Chrome plating** – tough, attractive, non-rusting. Chrome protects the steel in places where paint would probably be chipped.

⑥ **Petrol** – low boiling point, flammable. Liquid petrol easily turns into a gas which burns rapidly.

⑤ **Aluminium** – lightweight heat conductor. An aluminium engine weighs less than a normal steel engine. It also conducts heat away more effectively.

your use!

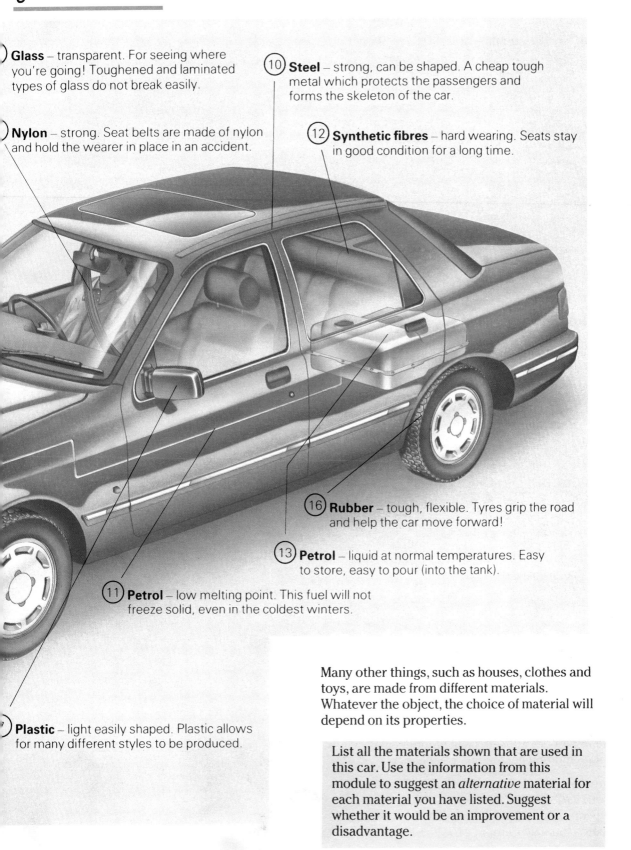

Glass – transparent. For seeing where you're going! Toughened and laminated types of glass do not break easily.

Nylon – strong. Seat belts are made of nylon and hold the wearer in place in an accident.

(10) **Steel** – strong, can be shaped. A cheap tough metal which protects the passengers and forms the skeleton of the car.

(12) **Synthetic fibres** – hard wearing. Seats stay in good condition for a long time.

(16) **Rubber** – tough, flexible. Tyres grip the road and help the car move forward!

(13) **Petrol** – liquid at normal temperatures. Easy to store, easy to pour (into the tank).

(11) **Petrol** – low melting point. This fuel will not freeze solid, even in the coldest winters.

Plastic – light easily shaped. Plastic allows for many different styles to be produced.

Many other things, such as houses, clothes and toys, are made from different materials. Whatever the object, the choice of material will depend on its properties.

List all the materials shown that are used in this car. Use the information from this module to suggest an *alternative* material for each material you have listed. Suggest whether it would be an improvement or a disadvantage.

Index

Photo acknowledgements

The references indicate page numbers and, where appropriate, the photo sequence.

Barnaby's *41/2*, (Micky White) *43/1*, (Norman Price) *43/2*, (John Edwards) *44/2*, *54/1*; British Telecommunications *54/1*; J Allan Cash *60*, John Cleare Mountain Camera *44/1*; Fire Research Station *58*; Sally & Richard Greenhill *32, 36, 38/2*; GeoScience Features *39, 50/1, 50/3, 50/4*; Adam Hart-Davis *52/3*, Trevor J Hill *43/3, 49/2, 52/3, 54/4*; Frank Lane Agency (Mark Newman) *41/1*, (Walter Rohdick) *50/2*, (Mike Thomas) *52/1*;

Cover photo: Pictor International Limited

MODULAR SCIENCE
for GCSE

MODULE *Humans as organisms*

All plants and animals are organisms. Many organisms do not have much control over the conditions in which they live. As a human being, you are unusual because you can make many choices about how you live. To help you make the right choices, this module looks at how the human body works.

Spread

Relevant National Curriculum Attainment Target: 2

Alive or dead!

Anything which is alive is called an **organism** – but how do you know if something is alive? These are the main features of life:

Eating

Breathing

Moving

Feeling

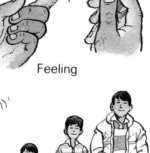

Reproducing

Excretion

Growing

Living the Good Life

There is more to being alive than just the seven features given above. An organism can get all it needs to stay alive but it may not be healthy. What do you think the word **healthy** means? Look at the people in these photographs. Do you think they are healthy? ▼

Can everyone expect to be healthy?

Your health can depend on where in the world you live. A woman in rural India will probably live to be about 45-50 years. A woman in a European town will probably live to be over 70 years old. The picture below tells you more.

- fewer children die in Europe
- there is plenty to eat
- people recover easily from simple illnesses
- cancer and heart disease are big threats
- these can be avoided by careful eating, exercising and by not smoking

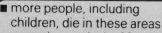

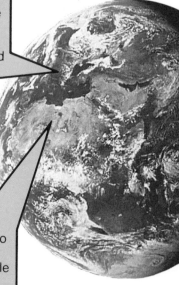

- more people, including children, die in these areas
- sometimes a lack of food is to blame
- most deaths are due to simple illnesses
- these could be avoided if more clean water and basic medicines were available

What happens if you stay healthy?

Your body is a complicated organism. It is made up of millions of tiny parts called **cells.** These cells work together to keep you alive. Your cells need certain conditions to keep them working properly. When you are 'healthy', your food and life style provide these conditions. If you stay healthy your body keeps working properly. This helps you to avoid illness and injury – even if you do fall ill, you get better more quickly. Being healthy makes you feel less tired and often lets you think more clearly. You will probably live longer too!

How do people stay healthy?

Think of the healthiest man (or boy) and woman (or girl) you know. Think of all the reasons why you consider them to be healthy. You should be able to think of at least five reasons.

Now write out a list of these reasons – put the most important ones at the top of the list.

Posters are often used to advise people of how to stay healthy. Look at these posters – what things are featured in them?

Draw a poster which would tell people about the most important reasons in your list. Try to make it as attractive, interesting and informative as you can.

What about you?

You are alive – so you must show the seven main features of life. But what exactly happens when you eat, breathe, grow or move? Why do you have to get rid of waste? What use is it to be able to react to what happens around you? You can learn a lot about yourself in this module. Once you know how your body works, you will also know how to stay healthy too!

2 Using energy

In a race, a sprinter uses enough energy to boil one cup of water.

Why do you need energy?

You need energy to do *anything*. Energy is used to keep warm, to go for a walk and even to grow. You also need energy just to stay alive – even when you may believe you are doing nothing! The amount of energy you need depends on what you do.

Where do you get your energy?

You get your energy from the food you eat. This is because your food is made of special chemicals which have energy stored inside them. For example, there is a lot of chemical energy stored in foods such as pasta. Your body can release this chemical energy from the food. This energy is used for warmth, movement, growth, or even just staying alive.

If humans don't get enough of energy from their food, their health may suffer. A child would become very tired and would not grow much. An old person would feel cold all the time and could even die from getting too cold.

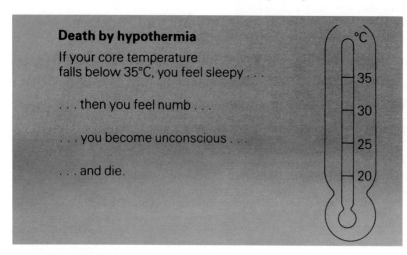

Death by hypothermia

If your core temperature
falls below 35°C, you feel sleepy . . .

. . . then you feel numb . . .

. . . you become unconscious . . .

. . . and die.

°C

35

30

25

20

Energy for warmth

Some energy is needed to keep your main body organs warm. The temperature of these organs is called your body's **core temperature**. To keep these organs working properly, your body's **core temperature** must be kept above 35°C. But your body loses heat energy all the time. If too much heat is lost, your core temperature will fall below 35°C. When this happens, you are suffering from **hypothermia**.

Dying from the cold

As well as eating enough energy-rich food, warm clothes and hot drinks can help to prevent hypothermia. The heat from the drinks warms the body from the 'inside-out' and the clothes help to keep that heat in.

Old people may suffer from hypothermia in winter, but others can be at risk too. Far away from the shore, the sea can be freezing cold – especially in winter. If someone falls in, the ice-cold water soon soaks through their clothes. This can cause hypothermia in minutes!

The high cost of heating a home in winter can put old people at risk from hypothermia.

Energy for movement

Walking and running use energy – but so do all other movements; eating, talking, writing and breathing. Any movement needs energy to make it happen. The bigger the movement, the more energy is needed.

Most sports involve a lot of movement. These bar charts show you why you get hot when you are more active.

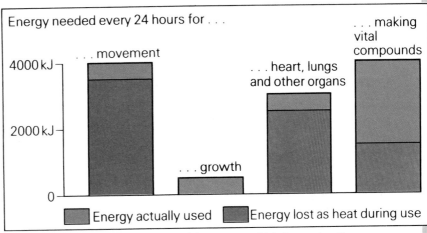

Energy needed every 24 hours for . . .

. . . movement
. . . growth
. . . heart, lungs and other organs
. . . making vital compounds

4000 kJ
2000 kJ
0

☐ Energy actually used   ☐ Energy lost as heat during use

Although energy is used for many things, most of it is lost as heat!

Energy for growth

You have grown in size and weight since you were born. As you grow, you use energy to help make the cells of which your body is made. Even when you have stopped growing you still need to make new cells to replace old ones as they die off. You can lose 4 million skin cells in a lesson! They just die and eventually fall off. So you need energy all the time to make new cells.

Energy to stay alive

At night while you are fast asleep, your body is still active. Breathing, repairing cells, fighting infections – these all involve important chemical reactions which keep you alive. Energy is needed to keep these reactions going. These important reactions carry on non-stop, so you need a constant supply of energy from food to stay alive. The table shows you that even when you sleep you use as much energy as the lightbulb in your room.

Activity	Energy used in 1 minute (measured in kilojoules)
Lying still	5 kJ
Sitting	7 kJ
Walking	10 kJ
Dancing	30 kJ
Running	44 kJ
Swimming	46 kJ
Skiing	64 kJ

cold water → hot water

1 Energy is used for all kinds of movements. Write down two other things energy is used for.

2 a Where does your energy come from?
   b Why do marathon runners eat lots of pasta before a race?

3 Why do you get hot when you run around a lot?

4 a Who do you think would use up most energy, someone who is sleeping or someone who is running? Why?
   b Who needs more energy *in total* – two people dancing or twelve people sleeping?

5 a What happens to your body when you suffer from hypothermia?
   b Why do you think that old people are more likely to die from hypothermia than young people?

3 What are you eating?

Chemicals for dinner!

The food you eat gives you the energy and materials you need to keep your body working properly. Most food contain many different chemicals. Scientists divide these chemicals into five main groups: carbohydrates; fats; proteins; minerals; vitamins.

Different foods contain different amounts of these chemicals. This picture shows an example of the British diet. It may look like 'just food', but it contains the many chemicals you need to stay alive.

Carbohydrates

Carbohydrates are chemicals that are used by your body to *store* energy for a short time. They can *produce* energy quickly when you need it. Carbohydrate foods are usually cheap and filling foods, eg, bread, rice, pasta and flour.

Fats

Fats are chemicals that are used to *store* energy for a long time. Fats cannot release energy quickly. This means it takes a long time for your body to use up any stores of fats. They also help to *insulate* your body so that you do not lose a lot of heat. Butter, margarine, meat and most fried foods contain a lot of fat.

Proteins

Proteins are used to help your body *grow*. They are used to make new cells and to repair damaged ones. If you do not get enough protein in your food, growth stops. Your body then has to use proteins already inside your body. This means your muscles start to waste away. Proteins may be used to give energy, but only if you do not get enough carbohydrate or fat. Meat, eggs, cheese and nuts all contain proteins.

Minerals

Minerals are simple chemicals which are found in tiny amounts in your food. They are substances such as calcium, iron and iodine. These minerals are essential for cells to work efficiently. Iron is needed to make haemoglobin – a complex chemical which plays a vital role in the breathing process.

Vital vitamins

Vitamins are usually complex chemicals, but they are given simple names: vitamin A, vitamin C, and so on. They are found in small amounts in most foods. Vitamins help to make cells work efficiently. You cannot store many vitamins or minerals in your body, so you need constant supplies of both.

Vegetables contain minerals and vitamins.

	What is it needed for?	What happens if you don't get it?
Vitamin A	To keep your lung tissues healthy. For light-sensitive cells in the eye	Lung infections Blindness
Vitamin B	To help many of the chemical reactions in your body	Tiredness, weakness, paralysis, and a disease called Beri Beri
Vitamin D	To help make use of minerals to make bones	Softening of bones and deformity (rickets).

Mineral	What it is needed for?	What happens if you don't get any?
Iron	To make **haemoglobin** in red blood cells	Tiredness, sleepiness (Anaemia)
Iodine	To make certain hormones. These control reactions in your body.	Possible weight increase swelling of the neck (goitre)
Calcium	Growth of bones and teeth	Brittle bones, teeth decay quickly

Some of the vitamins and minerals you need to stay healthy.

Fibre

Some foods contain a very tough material called fibre. This is not used by your body as a food. But it is still very important because the fibre helps to *clean* your gut. It can even soak up dangerous chemicals. Brown bread, brown rice, salads, fruit and vegetables all have a lot of fibre.

Food for thought

Look at the table below. Can you find any foods which you normally eat? Do you think you get enough of each type of chemical? Do you get too much of some others?

Carbohydrates	Fats	Proteins	Fibre, Minerals and Vitamins
High content BISCUITS, CHOC, CRISPS, Chips	CRISPS, cheese, BISCUITS, CHOC	cheese, egg	RICE, cheese, eggs
RICE, BAKED BEANS, Spuds, eggs	chips, egg	CHOC, BISCUITS, CRISPS, BAKED BEANS	BISCUITS, CHOC, egg
Low content egg, Cheese	BAKED BEANS, eggs, RICE	eggs, chips, RICE	chips, CRISPS, BAKED BEANS

1 What are the five main things that you find in the foods you eat?

2 What foods would you eat to:
 a give you energy?
 b help you grow?
 c help your body work efficiently?

3 What else is found in some foods that your body also needs?

4 Choose three foods from the table shown above that *together* would give you all the things your body needs from food.

4 Eating the right amount

A balanced diet

Are you on a diet? In fact your **diet** is the food you usually eat. When people say they are 'going on a diet' they mean a 'special diet'. This means that they change the amounts and the types of food they eat. On a **balanced diet** you only eat the foods that your body needs. If you get the balance wrong and eat too little or too much of one food your health will suffer. If you eat too much carbohydrate for example, your body will turn it into fat. This will then be stored around your stomach, hips and legs – and you will become overweight. The results can even be fatal!

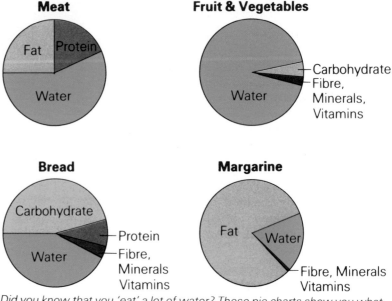

Did you know that you 'eat' a lot of water? These pie charts show you what your food is made of.

What do you need?

The *kind* of food you eat is important but so is the *amount* of food you eat. Each person needs different amounts of different foods. Why? It all depends on what age and sex they are and what they do. The charts show how people's needs can vary. They show the daily needs of fairly active people. Where do you fit in?

Teenagers need about the same amount of food as adults. This is because a lot of protein and energy is needed for growth.

Boys generally need more food than girls because boys grow to be bigger and heavier than girls. Although women usually need slightly less food than men, if a woman is pregnant she needs much more. After all, she is eating for two!

These bar charts show the masses of carbohydrate, fats and proteins needed by humans. The energy stored in each type of food is in red.

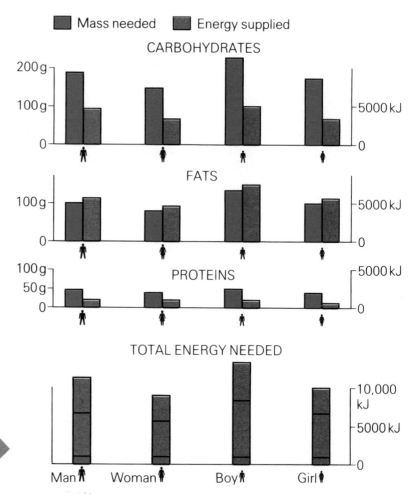

A poor diet

If the food you eat does not match your body's needs, then your diet is not balanced. In extreme cases a person may not get any carbohydrate or may take in too much fat. In each case their body will not get the nutrition needed in order to live a healthy life. Sometimes people suffer from **malnutrition**. This means the food in their usual diet does not match their food needs. Malnutrition can be caused by eating too much food as well as too little. The effects of malnutrition kill people, especially children. Over 40 million people die each year from a range of illnesses that are related to their diet.

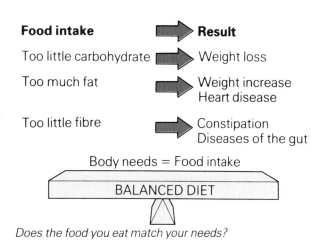

Food intake	→	Result
Too little carbohydrate	→	Weight loss
Too much fat	→	Weight increase Heart disease
Too little fibre	→	Constipation Diseases of the gut

Body needs = Food intake

BALANCED DIET

Does the food you eat match your needs?

What do you eat?

The tables below each picture show what these people eat in one average day. Two cases show malnutrition – one from eating too much, the other from eating too little. Which are they? Who has the most balanced diet?

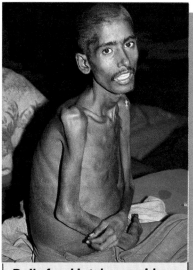

Daily food intake provides:	
Energy	18 600 J
Carbohydrate	270 g
Fat	180 g
Protein	58 g
Fibre	X

Daily food intake provides:	
Energy	9 300 J
Carbohydrate	196 g
Fat	48 g
Protein	28 g
Fibre	✓✓

Daily food intake provides:	
Energy	2 100 J
Carbohydrate	45 g
Fat	2 g
Protein	6 g
Fibre	✓

1
  a What is meant by a diet?
  b What is your usual diet?

2 What must be "balanced" in a balanced diet?

3 What are two effects of having a diet that is not balanced.

4 Explain what each person in the pictures above must do in order to balance their diet.

5 Which sort of foods should each person eat so that their diets will be balanced? (You may need to use the information on pages 66 and 67).

5 What happens when you eat?

Why do you eat?

You may think you eat just because you get hungry – but this isn't the only reason! The cells of your body need a constant supply of chemicals. These give the energy you need to live and grow. When you eat, you chew on food and swallow it. But what happens next? The chemicals in the food still have to get around your body.

Sometimes during hospital treatment, patients get the chemicals their bodies need without having to swallow anything. The chemicals that they need go directly from a drip feed into their bloodstream. These chemicals are then taken to all the cells in the body. These drips often contain glucose – a simple carbohydrate which will dissolve in blood. Glucose gives the patient the energy needed to get better.

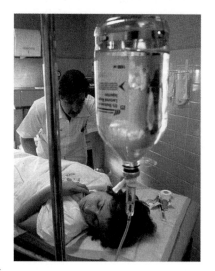

Glucose from this bottle flows down a drip feed, through a needle in the patient's arm and passes into their blood.

Getting food out of your gut

The chemicals in the food you eat must get from your gut into the **blood vessels** that surround your gut. Once the chemicals get into your blood, they can travel to every cell.

But your food is not usually made up of simple chemicals. For example, starch is a complex chemical – unlike glucose, it will not dissolve in your blood. This means that starch must be broken down into simple soluble chemicals. If this does not happen, the starch will stay in your gut.

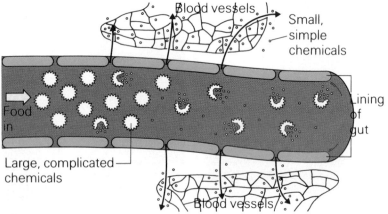

A simple chemical can pass out of your gut and into your bloodstream.

Breaking down your food

Your body has special substances that can help to break down the food you eat. These substances are called **enzymes**. When you eat some food, the enzymes in your gut mix with the complex chemicals in the food. Starch is an example of a complex carbohydrate. Through the action of enzymes, the starch you eat is *broken down* into a smaller carbohydrate called glucose. Glucose can then enter your blood by going through your gut.

Complex chemicals (such as starch) can be 'broken down' into simple chemicals (such as glucose) by enzymes.

The stages of digestion

The whole process of breaking down your food into **soluble** substances is called **digestion**. In digestion, the food that you eat is changed into something that your body can use.

The process is a slow one which starts at the entrance of your gut – the **mouth**. Here your food is chewed. This breaks it into small pieces. Some enzymes and other body chemicals also mix with the food in the mouth.

Then the chewed food is swallowed and it is churned (mixed up) in the **stomach**. Other enzymes and chemicals are added here.

The mixture then moves into the **small intestines**. It is in this part of the gut that simple chemicals are made from your food. These can then escape into the bloodstream.

Digestion is a series of slow chemical reactions. This is the most important part of digestion – changing your food into simple chemicals.

Some chemicals from food (such as fibre) are not digested. The fibre in the waste helps to clean the gut and to absorb some chemicals that would harm you. Finally the waste collects at the **rectum** where it is ejected.

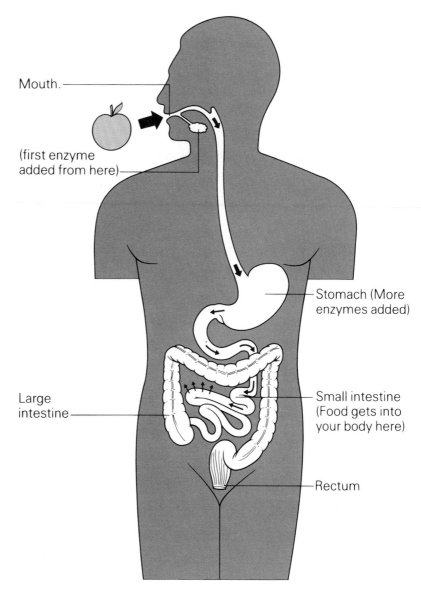

Mouth.

(first enzyme added from here)

Stomach (More enzymes added)

Large intestine

Small intestine (Food gets into your body here)

Rectum

1. What is the difference between starch and glucose?

2. Are starch and glucose similar in any way?

3. What is an enzyme and what does it do?

4. Why does chewing help digestion?

5. Why are people who eat lots of foods which contain fibre less likely to suffer from problems with their gut?

6 Every breath you take

Glucose is used up by your body to give you energy.

'Finding' the energy

When you start to run you may be relaxed but soon you may be red-faced, gasping for air and tired! In very long races 'drinks stations' are provided. Glucose drinks help to give the runner more energy. But the runner also needs oxygen from the air.

Oxygen and glucose **react** together to release **energy.** But a lot of this energy is released as heat. This why you feel hot after running. **Carbon dioxide** gas and **water** are also produced when oxygen and glucose react together. This process is called **respiration**. Here is an equation (in words) which describes the respiration reaction:

$$\text{Glucose} + \text{Oxygen} \longrightarrow \textbf{Energy} + \text{Carbon dioxide} + \text{water}$$

Breathing – why bother?

How do you get oxygen into your body? Your **lungs** do this important job. How do you get the carbon dioxide gas out of your body? Again you use your lungs. They **exchange** oxygen in the air for carbon dioxide in your blood. The water formed by respiration also needs to be removed. Can you think of any ways that water is lost? (You can find out more about water loss on page 82 and 83).

Fresh air in

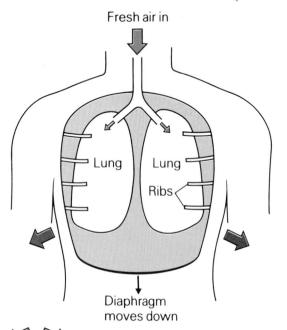

Lung Lung

Ribs

Diaphragm moves down

  Ribs move apart, chest expands

Used air out

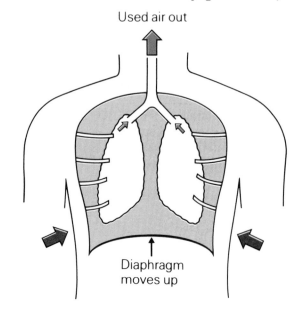

Diaphragm moves up

Ribs move together, chest contracts

Your chest and diaphragm muscles suck fresh air into your lungs and push used air out.

Your lungs—the great exchange

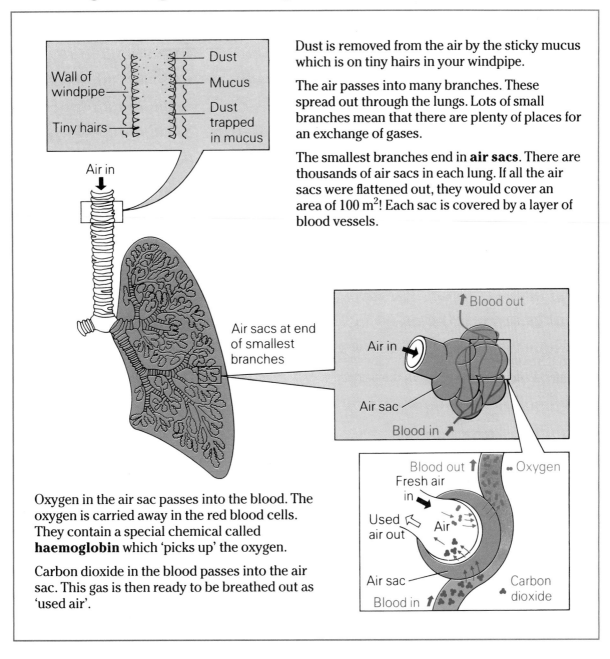

Dust is removed from the air by the sticky mucus which is on tiny hairs in your windpipe.

The air passes into many branches. These spread out through the lungs. Lots of small branches mean that there are plenty of places for an exchange of gases.

The smallest branches end in **air sacs**. There are thousands of air sacs in each lung. If all the air sacs were flattened out, they would cover an area of 100 m^2! Each sac is covered by a layer of blood vessels.

Oxygen in the air sac passes into the blood. The oxygen is carried away in the red blood cells. They contain a special chemical called **haemoglobin** which 'picks up' the oxygen.

Carbon dioxide in the blood passes into the air sac. This gas is then ready to be breathed out as 'used air'.

1.
a What two things do you need for respiration?
b What three things do you get from respiration?

2.
a Your lungs do two important jobs. What are they?
b What causes air to go in and out of your lungs?

3. How many desk tops would your lungs cover if they were folded out flat?

4. Marathon runners can get glucose from a 'drinks station'. Where do you get your glucose from? (You may need to look at page 74)

5.
a Where do you get oxygen from?
b Why is oxygen important?
c Explain why it is dangerous to put a plastic bag over your face.

7 Blood – supplying your needs

What does your blood do?

In many simple living organisms their body is made up of just one 'unit' called a cell. The chemicals that are needed for life are all inside this single cell. More complicated organisms have lots of cells. These organisms, such as humans, need to transport chemicals from one cell to another and their blood system does this job. An average 16 year old needs about 4 litres of blood to transport everything around the body.

If people have lost blood in an accident they can be given **blood transfusions.** This means giving them some 'new' blood to 'top up' their blood supply. Look at this picture. There is a small plastic bag hanging on the right which contains blood. The blood flows down the tube, then through a needle in the man's hand and into his body.

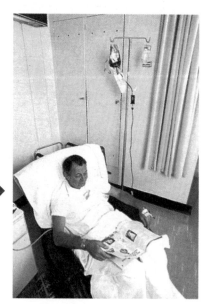

What is in your blood

Blood is a mixture of many different chemicals and cells. These all have different jobs to do. In the diagram you can see what is in your blood and what the different things do.

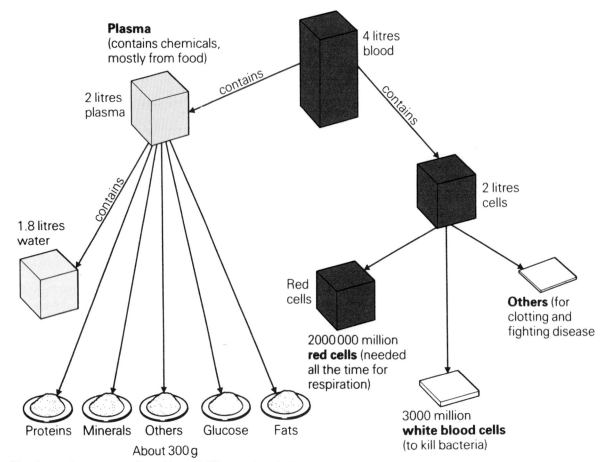

Blood contains water, cells and lots of different chemicals

Is everyone's blood the same?

When people bleed, it's always red, that's for sure! You have seen that blood contains many different chemicals and cells. But not all blood is exactly the same. There are four main types of human blood – O, A, B and AB – each of which contains slightly different chemicals.

The most common types are O and A; about 9 out of 10 people have either type of O or type A blood. These four types of blood are known as **blood groups**. If blood from the wrong group is used in a blood transfusion, the patient can become very ill. This is why careful checks are made before a blood transfusion.

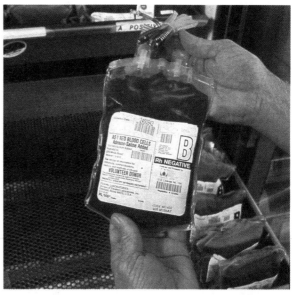

A blood 'bank' – notice that blood from the different groups is labelled clearly.

Bringing oxygen to every cell

All the cells in your body need oxygen to stay alive. It is your red blood cells that supply oxygen to all parts of your body. The red blood cells do this because they can join loosely with the oxygen. This is then carried around your body in the blood. The oxygen is then allowed to 'break off' to go to the cells which need it.

Carbon monoxide is a poisonous gas found in car fumes and cigarette smoke. It stops red blood cells from doing their job by blocking them up. The small amounts of carbon monoxide in cigarettes kill off muscle cells in your heart. This is why smoking weakens your heart. Large amounts of carbon monoxide can even kill you.

Oxygen moves easily from the lungs into the red blood cells. It easily breaks off easily to reach other cells.

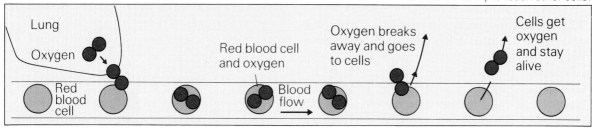

Carbon monoxide also moves easily into red blood cells – but blocks them up permanently.

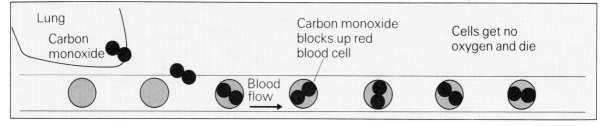

1 What happens in a blood transfusion?

2
 a How much water does your blood contain?
 b Where do the chemicals in your blood come from?

3 How does cigarette smoking damage your heart?

4 Why do you think your blood contains more red blood cells than white blood cells.

8 Your heart – a muscular pump

On the beat

Everything your body needs to stay alive can be found in your blood – oxygen, sugar, water and many other substances. A network of tubes called **blood vessels** pass through every part of your body. Blood is pumped along these tubes by your heart.

Your heart is made of **muscles**. These muscles form four hollow chambers. If the muscles of your heart tighten (**contract**), the blood is squeezed out of the chambers. This contraction pumps the blood out of your heart and around the body. **Valves** stop the blood from moving the wrong way through the heart. The sound of your heartbeat is the noise of these valves opening and closing.

The muscles of your heart must contract in a special order if your blood is to be pumped efficiently.

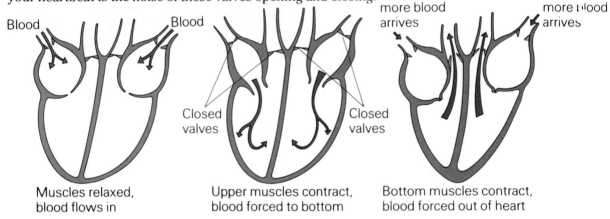

Blood | Blood

more blood arrives | more blood arrives

Closed valves | Closed valves

Muscles relaxed, blood flows in

Upper muscles contract, blood forced to bottom

Bottom muscles contract, blood forced out of heart

Heart and lungs

When your blood arrives at your heart from your other organs, it does not contain a lot of oxygen. But it does contain a lot of carbon dioxide – a product of respiration. Blood from your heart is first pumped from your heart to your **lungs**. When you breathe in 'fresh' air, red blood cells in this blood take up oxygen. At the same time, the carbon dioxide gas comes out of your blood in the lungs. It is breathed out in the 'used' air. The blood then returns to your heart.

Heart and Body

The blood now contains a supply of oxygen. Th heart then pumps this blood along large vessels called **arteries**. These take the blood to the major organs such as your brain, liver, kidneys and gut. These organs use up the oxygen in the blood during respiration.

The blood then returns from the organs to the heart. The blood does this by passing along blood vessels called **veins**. Once it is back in the heart, the blood is again pumped to the lungs, so that more oxygen can get into the blood.

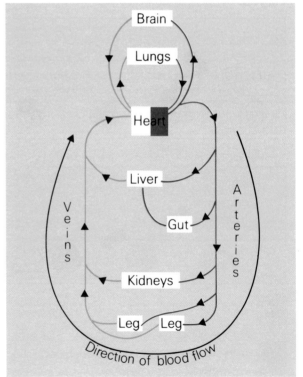

Brain
Lungs
Heart
Liver
Gut
Kidneys
Leg Leg
Veins
Arteries
Direction of blood flow

A simple view of how your blood flows around your body.

Supply lines

Some blood vessels carry a lot of blood but others can carry only a little. Their size and shape depends on where they are and what they have to do.

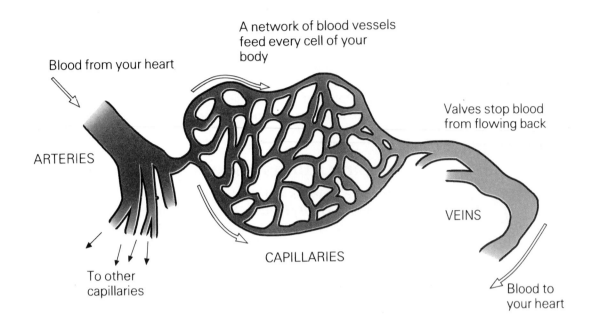

Blood from your heart

A network of blood vessels feed every cell of your body

Valves stop blood from flowing back

ARTERIES

VEINS

To other capillaries

CAPILLARIES

Blood to your heart

Large amounts of blood flow through the **arteries**. They bring blood to the major organs. The blood is under high pressure here so the walls of arteries are thick and strong.

Excess fat in your diet may cause blockages to occur in arteries. If there are any blockages, the results may be fatal.

Small amounts of blood flow through the **capillaries**. These narrow tubes can reach even the smallest cells in the body. This means vital chemicals can get directly from a capillary into most cells in the body.

There are thousands and thousands of capillaries in your body. They link your arteries to your veins.

Capillaries join up to form **veins**. These take blood back to the heart. A lot of blood flows through the veins, but the blood pressure is now low. This means the walls of veins do not need to be very thick.

Some small veins lie just under the skin. They can easily be seen as they have a faint blue colour.

1   What is the job of the heart?

2   Why is the blood pumped to your lungs first?

3   What are the names of the three types of blood vessels in the body?

4   Write down places in your body where you would find valves. What do they do?

5   Why do you need high blood pressure in the arteries?

9 Waste – life's leftovers

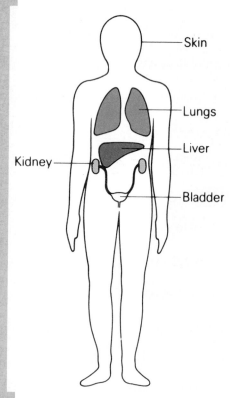

Each part of your body which is shown here helps to get rid of waste.

Labels: Skin, Lungs, Liver, Kidney, Bladder

From 'junk' food to waste products

Your food contains many substances such as carbohydrates, fats and proteins. Your gut breaks them down so that they can be absorbed and used by your body. As your body uses these chemicals, waste products are made. These must be removed or they will harm you. The removal process is called **excretion**.

Carbon dioxide is an example of a waste product. It is formed during respiration. Your **lungs** remove the waste carbon dioxide. There are other waste products and these are dealt with by one of three organs.

Keeping things under control

Your **liver**, **kidneys** and **skin** are three other organs that control and remove waste products. Your liver controls many of the chemicals in your body. Your kidneys control most of the removal of waste from the blood. The heat produced by reactions inside your body is also a waste product. It is your skin that controls the loss of waste heat from your body.

Life depends on the liver!

The blood in the vessels surrounding your gut contains many substances. This blood goes straight to your liver – your 'chemical factory'. In your liver, some of the proteins take part in chemical reactions. This produces a poisonous waste called **ammonia**. Your liver quickly changes the ammonia into a harmless chemical called **urea**. This 'safe waste' dissolves in the blood which flows out of your liver.

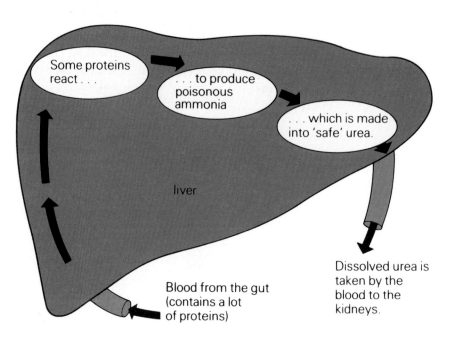

Some proteins react . . .

. . . to produce poisonous ammonia

. . . which is made into 'safe' urea.

liver

Blood from the gut (contains a lot of proteins)

Dissolved urea is taken by the blood to the kidneys.

Filtering through

You have two kidneys in your body. They *filter* your blood and remove the wastes. Blood is pumped into very thin tubes in your kidneys. Urea, glucose, water and other simple chemicals are forced out of the blood. Useful chemicals are absorbed back into your blood. Any waste substances, such as urea, are not absorbed back. This waste is then diluted with water and lost from your body as **urine**.

Skin deep

Your skin controls the loss of waste heat. It can do this by changing the flow of blood through your skin. When the blood is close to the surface, your skin looks red and heat passes from your blood through your skin. This heat is soon lost to the air and you cool down.

Some of the water and waste in your blood passes into sweat glands. These glands release the water and waste as sweat. The heat escaping through your skin causes the sweat to evaporate. This helps the heat to be lost even more quickly.

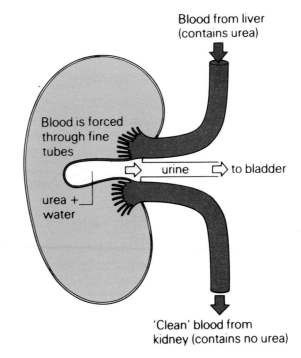

Your kidneys are very selective filters.

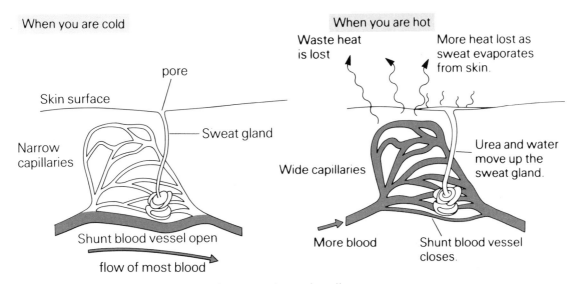

'When you're hot, you're hot!' – and your shunt vessels are closed!

1 Which organs of your body help remove waste?

2 a What happens to some of the proteins in your blood when they reach the liver?
b Why could this be dangerous?

3 a How does your liver deal with ammonia?
b What happens to the safe waste product made from ammonia?

4 a Explain how your kidneys remove waste from your body.
b What other waste products do you think could also be lost in your urine?

5 a Why is sweating important to your body?
b Why do you think you sweat more after running than walking?

10 Muscle & bone, a joint effort

Long-lasting protection....

Your bones are the hardest things in your body. Some bones have been found that are thousands of years old. Why do you need something so tough inside you? You have many vital organs in your body – if these get damaged you could die. Your chest has many bones just below the skin – these make up your rib-cage. This protects your heart and lungs from getting damaged.

....and a supporting role

Some organisms are supported by their surroundings. Certain jellyfish are completely supported by the water in which they float. You are surrounded only by air – this cannot support you. Your bones protect you but they also *support* your body. They can do this because they are linked together to form a **skeleton**. Without it you would collapse into a jumbled heap of organs and limbs!

On the move

Many of the bones in your skeleton are connected by special **joints**. These joints allow connected bones to move in certain directions. But what causes the bones to move? Every bone in your body has **muscles** fixed to it. You have to use chemical energy to make these muscles change length.

If a muscle becomes shorter, it will pull on the bone attached to it. The joint at the end of the bone twists round and the bone then moves in that direction.

Let's all pull together

Bones which have joints at the end usually have more than one muscle attached. These muscles work in pairs to let your carefully control the movement of the bones. This picture shows that you have two muscles to control movement of your knee.

If you want to keep your leg halfway up, both muscles will have to do some pulling. The top muscle will have to pull to keep your leg up. But the bottom muscle will have to pull to stop your leg from going up too far. The two muscles will have to work together, but pull *against* each other. When this happens, they are called an **antagonistic pair** of muscles.

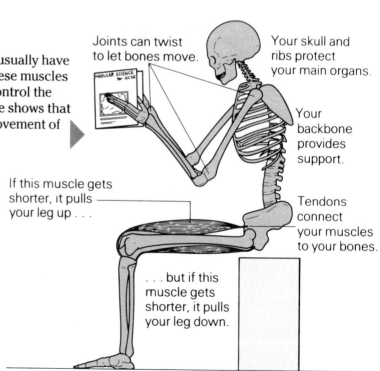

Joints can twist to let bones move.

Your skull and ribs protect your main organs.

Your backbone provides support.

If this muscle gets shorter, it pulls your leg up . . .

Tendons connect your muscles to your bones.

. . . but if this muscle gets shorter, it pulls your leg down.

Under careful control

How many ways can you bend your knee? The knee is a fairly simple joint – it can only twist forwards and backwards. What about your shoulder, wrist and neck? These joints are more versatile – they can move in many directions.

The bones which make up these joints have many antagonistic pairs of muscles attached to them. This allows you to control the movement of your arms, hands and head with accuracy. Imagine how difficult it would be to write a letter with a pen tied to your knee!

Taking the strain

When you hurt some part of your body, you try not to use it. For example, if you hurt your foot, you tend to limp, keeping your foot stiff to avoid bending it as you walk. This often makes other muscles in your leg and back start to feel sore. This is because these other muscles are part of a group of antagonistic pairs of muscles used in walking. By limping, you keep the strain off of your foot but you put extra strain on to other groups of muscles.

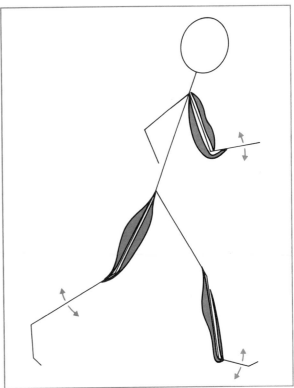

There are many antagonistic pairs of muscles in your body – and they often work in groups.

'Joint Action'

It is impossible for a single joint to be able to move in every direction – if it tried to, the bones would be twisted completely off the joint. But you can move your hand to touch anything around you. How do you manage to do this?

Think for a moment of how you get through a crowd of people. You can't usually walk in a straight line. You have to turn left and right as you walk along – but you get through. The same is true of moving your hand to a particular place – you may have to twist your shoulder a bit, bend your elbow and move your wrist. By moving more than one joint at a time, almost any movement is possible.

Like most movements, a gymnast's routine uses several joints at a time.

1 Complete these two sentences: Your bones _____ your vital organs from _____. Your bones are linked to form a _____ which _____ your body.

2 What causes your muscles to change length?

3 When you clean a blackboard, which joint twists the most? Draw a diagram to show how an antagonistic pair of muscles could make your arm move in this way.

4 Imagine your right arm is stretched out sideways. Which joints will you have to use to move your right hand *over* your head to scratch your left ear?

11 Getting hurt

Making a wrong move

Your body is always moving – even when you are asleep. These movements may be strong and fast, especially when playing sport. If your bones and joints are in the wrong position when you move them, you can get injured. The most common serious injuries are sprains, dislocations and fractures. If they are not treated immediately, these injuries can get much worse. People who are trained in 'First-Aid' usually know how to treat such injuries.

Around the bend

Your joints are made up of several parts. A joint connects two bones; these bones are usually separated by a piece of tough **cartilage**. The bones are held together in the joint by strong elastic strands called **ligaments**. Muscles make the bones move around the joint. These muscles are fixed to the bones by **tendons**. The tendons are usually found very close to the joint.

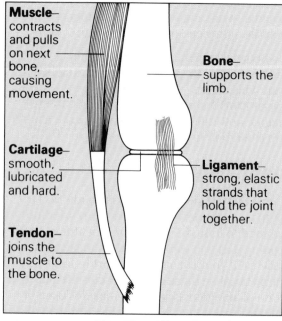

Muscle – contracts and pulls on next bone, causing movement.

Bone – supports the limb.

Cartilage – smooth, lubricated and hard.

Ligament – strong, elastic strands that hold the joint together.

Tendon – joins the muscle to the bone.

A typical joint – without your joints, you would not be able to move at all.

A hockey injury

The player's knee is damaged. What could have happened?

Forcing a reaction

If a strong sideways force acts on a joint, you may **sprain** the joint. This happens when the ligaments and tendons are over-stretched. The joint usually reacts by swelling up and becoming stiff and sore. By making it difficult or painful to use, your body protects the sprained joint. This is because it makes you rest the injury.

All out of joint

If the sideways force is very strong, the bones may be pulled completely out of place. This is called a **dislocation** – this is because the bone has been separated from the joint. All ligaments and tendons will be greatly over-stretched. It is important that only a trained person treats a dislocated joint – and quickly. This is because any further movement could easily tear the ligaments and tendons.

Sprain

Knee cap

Ligaments and muscles across the joint are over-stretched

Dislocation

Bones no longer meet at the joint.

Lower leg bones

Upper leg bone

Sticks and stones....

Very large forces will **fracture** your bones. A hard fall or a fast moving hockey stick or football boot may be enough to do this. Even the force from your own muscles can fracture your own bones. Some unlucky footballers have broken their kneecaps by kicking the ground instead of the ball. The muscle which makes the leg kick is attached to the knee cap. By kicking the ground, the leg stops moving – but the muscle keeps pulling and breaks the kneecap.

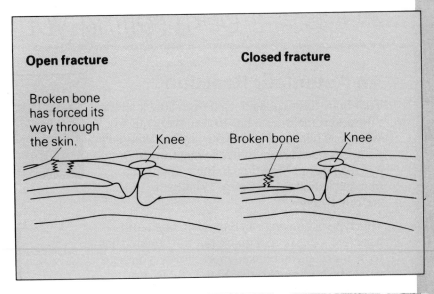

Help at hand – First Aid

First-Aid consists of various simple, sensible things you can do when someone is injured. It usually involves stopping injuries from getting worse. Serious injuries may need treatment by a doctor, but First Aid can help long before the doctor gets a chance to treat the injury.

Wherever there are a lot of people, someone may get injured. At sports events and pop concerts, St. John ambulance staff provide First-Aid. In factories and large offices, some of the workers will be trained as 'First-Aiders' – so will some of the teachers in your school.

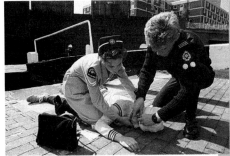

Simple First-Aid is easy to learn, but serious injuries need trained help.

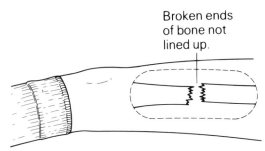

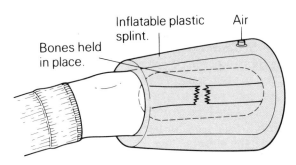

Any movement may cause the jagged broken bone to cut arteries, nerves or flesh. The splint supports the broken bone and lines the ends up preventing further damage.

1 Your bones and joints can suffer three types of serious injury. What are they?

2 Which five things are connected together to make a joint?

3 How does your body try to protect damaged joints?

4 What is the difference between a closed fracture and an open fracture?

5 Find out if any of your family or friends have ever suffered from a sprain, dislocation or a fracture? Try to get information about at least ten people's injuries. Draw up a table to show their age at the time of the injury suffered and how it was caused. Which is the most common injury?

12 Controlling your reactions

An Automatic Reaction

Your body has to defend itself from attack all the time and sometimes it has to react very quickly. When you blink suddenly, you may be defending yourself against something moving towards your eye. You do not have time to think about this blinking action, it just seems to happen 'automatically'!

This type of blinking can happen in one tenth of a second – this is very quick, but the blinking has to be quick. If you blinked more slowly, your eye would be hurt more often. Your sight is very important to you, so it is very difficult to stop this reaction.

Short circuiting the system

How can your senses get your muscles to react so quickly? Your body contains millions of **nerves**. These can receive and send little electrical messages to and from each other. Each of these nerves has a special job to do.

Some nerves can detect changes in the surroundings. These are called **sensory nerves**. These usually send messages all the time way back to your brain. This lets you decide what to do with the information from the nerve.

But sometimes the message does not reach your brain. If the message needs urgent action, it can get short-circuited by a **relay nerve**. These are found in your spine. The relay nerve sends the message straight to a nerve which controls a muscle. This type of nerve is called a **motor nerve**. When a motor nerve gets a message, it makes the muscle move.

The message makes a 'short-circuit' by going through the relay nerve instead of going through your brain. This 'short-circuit' means that the muscle can move much more quickly. This is how your body can react 'automatically' to sudden changes in your surroundings.

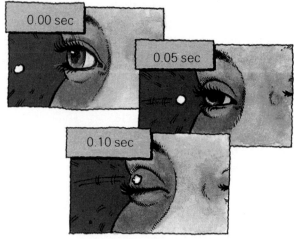

Even if you didn't notice something thrown at your eye until very late, your eyelid could still close in time.

Your reflex reactions are much faster than reactions you have to think about – you will drop a hot tray before you can shout in pain.

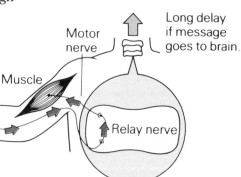

Relay nerves allow you to have very quick reactions.

Sensible Precautions

Your body has several 'warning systems' to protect you from injury. Your eyes are one example – how do they help to protect you? There are five such warning systems – sight, hearing, touch, taste and smell. These are called the five **senses**.

These senses provide you with information about your surroundings. You then use this information to guide your actions. For example, rotten food can make you sick, but if you start to eat some rotten food, you can quickly taste the rotten flavour. Your sense of taste has been able to warn you not to eat the food.

Your sight tends to dominate the other senses, but it can't do everything. Although you can only look in *one* direction at a time, your hearing 'listens' in *all* directions. You may not be able to see if something is hot or sharp, but a gentle touch will soon tell you.

Her sight shows her where to reach for the bar, so her eyes help to 'protect' her from falling.

Making sense of your senses

Very young children have to learn how to use their senses to control their actions. They are often slow or clumsy because they cannot make good use of reflex reactions. For example, they fall over a lot because they cannot control their muscles quickly enough to stay balanced upright. When they are older, they will run or walk or hop without any problems – because they will be using reflex reactions to keep their balance without even thinking about it.

Regular practice can develop new reflex reactions and can improve the speed of existing reflexes. Most sports require quick reactions of some kind – and the more you practice, the better you get at the game. This is because practice develops the particular reflex reactions which you need to be able to do well at the sport.

He won't catch the balloon because he can't control his eye reflexes – his eyes close when anything is near his face.

1
  a What are the five senses?
  b Which parts of your body are involved with which senses?

2
  a Explain what sensory nerves do.
  b Explain what motor nerves do.

3
  How can a sense of smell help to protect to you?

4
  Give examples of at least five kinds of reflex reactions. In each case explain what would happen if there was no reflex reaction.

5
  Find out two ways in which blind people overcome their lack of sight. Which senses do they use to help them do this?

13 Measuring fitness

Fit for what?

There are many different ways of describing how fit you are. You could be fit in terms of speed or stamina or agility. A sprinter may be able to run very fast over a short distance but may get very tired if he or she has to run several miles. A marathon runner can run for hours but may get exhausted by a little weight-training. So what does being 'fit' mean?

During any activity you do, your heart will be beating and you will be breathing. This means two good tests for fitness are:

- How fast does your heart go when you are active?
- How fast do you breathe in and out when you are active?

These people are all very fit, but they would soon get tired doing a different sport.

Activity and your heart

When you are active, your body has to work harder than usual. You have to use up a lot of energy to make yourself move – this energy comes from respiration. (You can read more about respiration on page 76.)

You need oxygen and glucose to help you to release energy during respiration. The energy is needed by your muscles, to make them move. How can the oxygen and glucose get to your muscles?

The oxygen and glucose are carried around your body by your blood. The more active you are, the more energy you need. This means you need to supply more oxygen and glucose to your muscles. To do this, your heart must pump more blood around your body. So, the more active you are, the faster and harder your heart will beat. A fit person's heart can do this easily – but an unfit person will put a great strain on their heart.

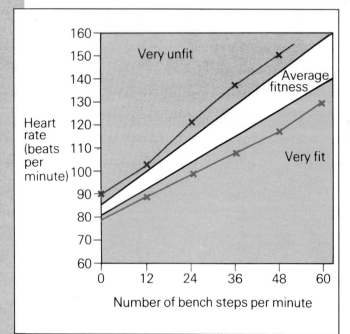

Heart rate increases when you are active. The red line gives the results for an unfit boy (weighing 50kg). The blue line is for a fit boy of the same weight.

Activity and your lungs

How do you get a lot of oxygen into your blood when you are active? You need to breathe in and out more quickly *and* more deeply. Deep breaths in and out mean you take in more fresh air and get rid of more used air.

Breathing out is very important – it gets rid of waste carbon dioxide from your blood. The more energy you use up when you are active, the more waste carbon dioxide is produced. This has to be got rid of. If you don't get rid of it, you will feel dizzy and faint.

How fit are you?

You can test your fitness by finding out exactly how much your heart rate increases when you become active. If you are fit, your heart rate will be low to start off with. As you exercise, your heart rate will not increase by much. You can check this on the heart rate graph on the previous page.

Another way of checking your fitness is to find out your **recovery time**. This is the amount of time that you have to wait for your heart rate to return to normal. Your recovery time gets shorter as you get fitter.

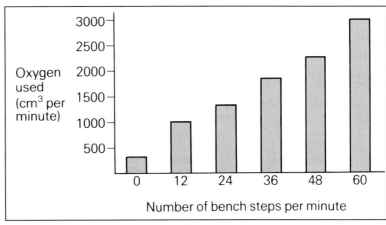

When resting you use about 300cm³ of oxygen a minute. How many times more oxygen do you use after doing 60 bench steps in one minute?

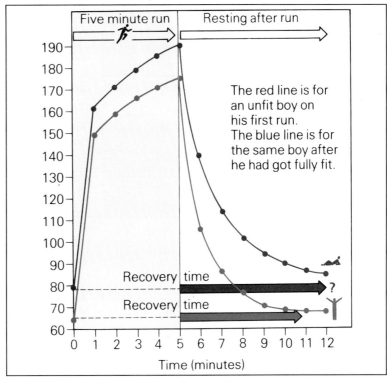

By measuring heart rate during and after a five-minute run you can find out your recovery time.

1 What are the two best ways to test for fitness?

2 Why does your blood need to move more quickly when you are active?

3 Why do you produce more carbon dioxide when you are active?

4 **a** A boy has a heart rate of 130 beats per minute after doing 48 bench steps in 60 seconds – is he fit or unfit?
   b If his heart rate was 160 beats a minute would he be fit or unfit?

5 Think of a simple (*but safe*) way in which you could measure the volume of air you breathe out. Describe your idea. Use a diagram to show how it could be done.

14 Keeping fit

It's up to you

If you take care of your body, you should remain fit and healthy. But if you neglect your health, your body can be seriously damaged within just a few years.

In Europe and North America, disease and malnutrition are not common – thanks to modern medicines, clean water supplies and a good supply of food. But serious health problems still occur. Why should this be so?

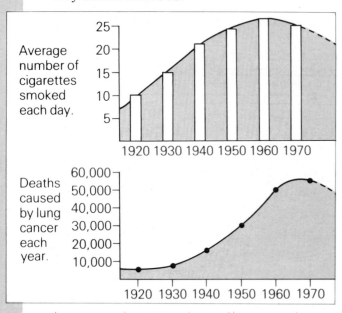

Increases in cigarette smoking and increases in lung cancer over the same period.

Smoking

When someone smokes a cigarette, their heart rate gets faster. Their blood vessels get narrower and this makes the flow of blood more difficult. The increase in heart rate and the poor blood flow means that their heart has to work much harder to pump blood around the body. Also carbon monoxide gas in the smoke poisons some of the muscles of your heart.

The cigarette smoke contains tar and large smoke particles. These get stuck in the small air sacs in your lungs. This makes it difficult to breathe easily. Smoking weakens your heart and blocks up your lungs – so if you want to be fit, don't smoke!

As well as affecting your fitness, smoking is a major cause of several lung diseases. These diseases, such as lung cancer, will eventually kill you.

Diet

Some of the fats produced from your food can stick to the walls of your arteries. These fatty deposits can get larger and may even block an artery. The coronary artery supplies blood to your heart muscles. If this artery becomes blocked, your heart will stop beating. This is called a heart attack and can be fatal.

Not all fats cause these problems. There is a special group of fats called **polyunsaturated fats**. These are safe to eat because they do not block arteries.

You should exercise regularly to keep the heart muscles in good condition. Any exercise will do – as long as it makes your heart rate go up. A lack of exercise means that the heart does not get strengthened. Your body will also become fat and heavy. This extra weight will put a greater strain on your body, and also your heart.

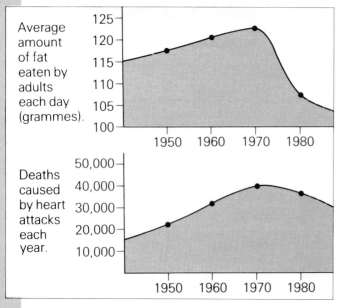

After many adults reduced the fat in their diet, the number of deaths due to heart attacks started to fall.

Alcohol

Alcohol is a drug which affects your brain and your reflexes. This is why people who are drunk slur their words and become clumsy. The capillaries below the skin become larger and make the skin look red. In large or frequent doses, alcohol is a poison which can seriously damage your liver and nerves. But small doses make people feel relaxed and this is why it is a widely used drug.

Many people drink alcohol in pubs, but drivers should not drink and drive.

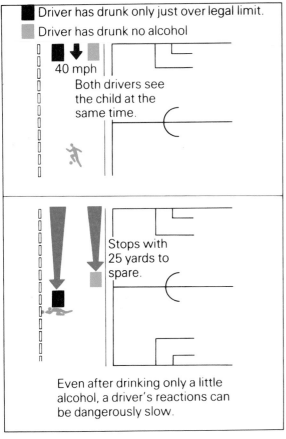

■ Driver has drunk only just over legal limit.

▨ Driver has drunk no alcohol

40 mph

Both drivers see the child at the same time.

Stops with 25 yards to spare.

Even after drinking only a little alcohol, a driver's reactions can be dangerously slow.

Alcohol slows the reflexes and drivers cannot stop quickly enough in an emergency.

This man is blowing into an electronic breathalyser. The police officer will now be able to tell if he is too drunk to drive.

1 Write down four ways in which smoking makes your heart do extra work.

2 What has happened to
a the amount of tobacco smoked each year since 1920?
b The number of deaths due to lung cancer over the same time?
c Do the graphs suggest any link between smoking and lung cancer? Explain your answer.

3 Look at the graphs which show fat intake and heart attacks. Do you think the two may be related? Explain your answer.

4 a Why is alcohol a popular drug?
b Why is it dangerous?

5 Look at the braking diagram above. What does it tell you about the risks of 'drinking and driving'?

15 What a life you lead!

Decisions, Decisions

You begin making decisions about your life at a very early age. For example, whether to eat your dinner or to go out to see your friends. Even these decisions can affect your life. Having 'no dinner' may mean you go hungry for the rest of the day. There are many people in the world who cannot make decisions about the food they eat. They have no choice – because they can't get any food. Forty million of them die each year from starvation. That's equal to two out of every three people in Britain.

Decisions and consequences

You may be fortunate enough to be able to make decisions about your life. You may also be unfortunate to suffer the consequences. The case studies show how three people live their lives. They have to make decisions about their lives all the time...just like you.

This child may be lucky to get a decent meal soon. How many times in a week are you that lucky?

Case studies

The following descriptions about Jamie, Meta and Simon are from other members of their class, read the descriptions carefully and pick out as much information as possible.

Jamie is 14 and plays football for the school and the Town team. He trains about 4 times a week and usually plays twice a week.

His parents make sure he eats the right foods and even give him a special packed lunch. Although he plays a lot of football, he doesn't ever seem to get tired out.

He is friendly with some older boys and has started drinking cider and smoking cigarettes on his way home from training and matches.

Meta is 16 and is usually top of the class. She does not join in the sports activities because she is often too tired.

She hardly eats at all during the day and her best friend says that after meals at home she is sick.

She says she is cold and she always looks ill.

She is very fussy about her food and doesn't like to eat fruit and vegetables.

Simon is nearly 15 and wishes he wasn't at school. He is over-weight and always tries to get out of sports.

He likes to **watch** sports but hates to play them. He usually watches us from the touchline, eating sweets and chocolates while we run around.

If he has to run for a bus, he is always the last there and he gets really hot and goes red in the face.

What would you advise Jamie, Meta and Simon to do so as to live a healthier life? Make a life plan for one or more of the people. In each life plan:
  a) list the things they do that **may do them harm;**
  b) list the things that are **good for them;**
  c) plan what they should do to have a **life they will enjoy.**

You may find some useful ideas by looking back through this module.

Index

(refers to page numbers)

Photo acknowledgements

The references indicate page numbers and, where appropriate, the photo sequence.

Barnaby's *68/2, 73/1, 73/3, 93/1*; J Allan Cash *66/1, 66/2, 73/2*; Health Education Authority *67/4, 67/5*; Hutchinson *94*; Carmilla Jessel *89/2*; Metropolitan Police *93/2*; St John's Ambulance *87*; Science Photo Library *65, 67/3, 70, 74, 78*; Sporting Pictures *68/1, 85/2, 89/1, 90*; Peter Vine *84/1*.

Cover photo: Science Photo Library

MODULAR SCIENCE
for GCSE

MODULE

Communication and control

What must happen to the sound of a DJ in a radio studio before you can hear it on your radio? Quite a lot – the sound has to detected, processed, transmitted as radio waves, then these have to be detected by your radio, processed and output as sound for you to hear. This module will help you to find out more about sound – in the form of speech, music and noise. It will also show you how control of electronic systems helps people to detect and output sound for many different uses.

Spread

Relevant National Curriculum Attainment Target: AT4(iv)

1 How you communicate

To talk is human

Our ability to talk and communicate is one of the characteristics that mark us out from other animals. You have two systems for making and modifying sounds – your **vocal cords** and your **mouths**. Most talking uses a mixture of both, but ventriloquists develop their use of vocal cords so that they do not have to move their lips.

The pattern of sound in your voice is unique. People can imitate the voices of others, but if the sound pattern is looked at carefully, the characteristics of the voice can be recognised. This is how voice activated locks work – a computer analyses a sound and compares the pattern with one that has already been programmed into the computer's memory.

Patterns of sound can also be made by computers. This type of computer is known as a voice synthesiser.

Talk, talk, talk – do you think before you speak? How well do you communicate?

Key

1 lips
2 teeth and lips
3 teeth
4 alveolar
5 palate and alveolar
6 palate
7 velar
8 glottal

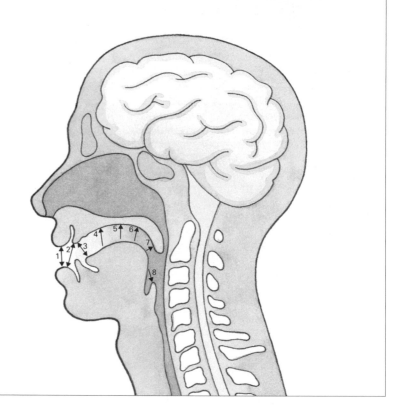

You use different parts of your mouth and throat to make different sounds. Can you work out what you use to say certain words?

Read my lips!

Some people with hearing difficulties, or who work in very noisy places, have developed the art of lip reading, so that they do not have to rely on hearing. Lip reading means watching carefully each shape of the lips and then assembling the message.

Some people have to rely on lip reading, rather than hearing, to understand others when they talk. Can you read this message?

1 Make these sounds (quietly!) and work out which goes with which area shown on the diagram on the opposite page. Concentrate on the sounds of the part of the word that is underlined in each case. <u>Co</u>ld, <u>Fee</u>t, <u>Ho</u>y, <u>Hue</u>, <u>Pi</u>p, <u>Shi</u>p, <u>Tape</u>, <u>Thi</u>nk

2 Sketch the diagram and add the results you get in question 1.

3 What other ways do we have to communicate with people who cannot hear?

4 What problems will there be facing a child who cannot hear? What suggestions could you make to help overcome these problems?

5 You have just moved from a school which encouraged group work and collaborative learning to one in which a policy of 'no-talking-in-lessons' is strictly enforced. Write a memo to the headteacher pointing out the advantages in being able to talk as part of the learning experience.

2 The listening ear

What the ear does

Your ear is the sense organ that enables you to hear and to balance. It is made up of a large number of delicate parts. These parts are protected by the bone of the skull, so they are difficult to see. Only the outer part of the ear, known as the **pinna** can normally be seen.

We can hear sounds if they are loud enough, and if their **frequency** (page 102) is in the range our ears can detect.

How the ear hears

The pinna is a large flap of skin that acts like a funnel. Sounds are collected by the pinna and travel along the ear canal to the **ear drum**. The sound waves make the ear drum vibrate. Movement of the ear drum makes the three small ear **ossicles** vibrate. These three small bones transmit the vibrations to the **oval window**. The ossicles are a system of levers, so the size of the vibrations is increased as it is transmitted through the ossicles – this increases the sensitivity of the ear.

Listening to yourself is an important part of learning to talk so you get the right sound and loudness. But you hear yourself through the air and the bones of your skull. How you hear yourself talk is different to what other people hear. That's why your voice sounds strange on a tape recorder.

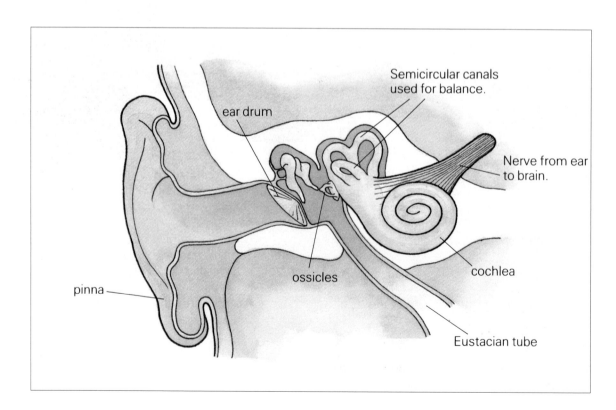

The inner ear

The **inner ear** or **cochlea** is made up of a bag of fluid floating inside more fluid. The bag of fluid is coiled up like a snail's shell (cochlea is Latin for snail). Inside the coiled bag are two sets of membranes joined by sensitive cells. When the oval window vibrates the vibrations pass through the cochlea. Different pitches of sound bend different parts of the cochlea. Different nerves lead from each part of the cochlea, so the brain can tell if the sound has a high or low pitch, or a mixture.

Young people can normally detect sound in the range between 20 Hz and 20 000 Hz. However the upper limit decreases as people get older.

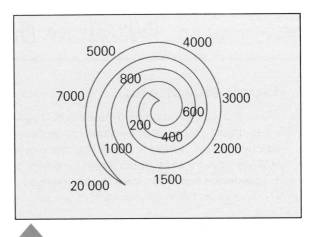

The cochlea of your ear is sensitive to sounds of different frequencies at different places in its coils. In this way your brain gets the message as to what sound is being made..

There are two windows into the inner ear. These are different shaped holes in the bone between the middle and inner ear. The oval shape allows the ear ossicles to pass vibrations to the cochlea. The round shape allows vibrations to be 'lost' from the inner ear, otherwise the vibrations would go on and on.

Look after your ears

As people get older, their ears become less sensitive. The ear canal may fill with wax, or the muscles controlling the ossicles may weaken. The ear drum may be damaged – a perforated ear-drum means that a hole has been torn in the membrane by a loud noise or an explosion. Total deafness may be the result of damage to the auditory nerve.

1. Make a list of the parts of the ear. Against each part write down what it looks like and what it does.

2. What are some of the common defects in hearing?

3. Apart from damaging our ears, why else is noise a nuisance?

4. Muffco has recently produced a new ear protector which cuts out 90% of external noise. Design a leaflet to go in the boxes of new protectors which explains how the ear works and encourages people to use ear protection.

Loud noises reduce sensitivity of the ear. Careful protection is necessary where people are exposed to very noisy environments for long periods.

3 What is sound?

Good vibrations

If you put your hand on your throat when you talk you can feel **vibrations**. These vibrations come out of your mouth as vibrations in the air. The vibrations are **sound waves** moving through the air. Sound is caused by vibrations. Wherever these vibrations can be passed on, you will get sound waves. Sound waves transfer energy through a substance. In this example energy is transferred from your vocal cords to your hand – the substance it is transferred through is air.

What sort of waves?

Sound waves are rather different from the 'up-and-down' waves you see at the sea. They are **longitudinal**, or 'push-pull' waves, best shown on a long spring. When one end of the spring is pushed, a wave passes *along* the spring. Some parts of the coil are pushed together, the next parts are pulled wider apart, while in the next part the coils are pushed together again and so on.

Air is springy as well. When sound waves pass through air 'push-pull' waves are set up, just as in the spring. However, it is molecules of gas that are pushed together and pulled apart, instead of the metal coils. The molecules vibrate with the same **frequency** as the sound.

Just like 'up-and-down' waves, 'push-pull' waves can have different **wavelengths** – the distance from the start of one area of pushing together to the next. They can have different **amplitudes** (sizes), caused by more or less pushing together. The greater the amplitude, the louder the sound.

In many ways it is convenient to represent longitudinal waves as 'up-and-down' waves – they are much easier to draw and to think about that way.

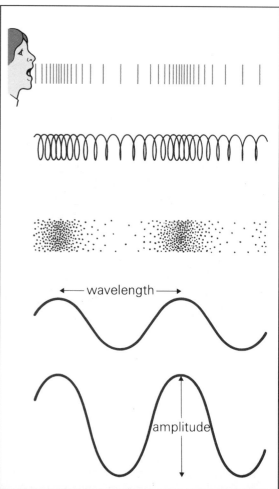

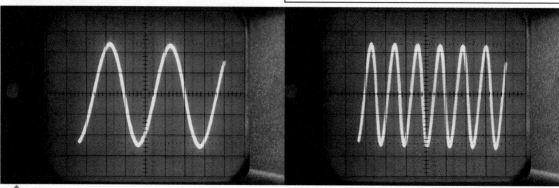

If sounds are played into an oscilloscope the sound trace is produced as an 'up' and 'down' wave.

Notes on notes

The frequency of a wave is the number of vibrations it makes in one second. This is measured in **Hertz**, named after Heinrich Hertz, a nineteenth century German scientist. A frequency of 10 Hertz means 10 wavelengths will pass in one second.

A musical note is a sound with one particular frequency. For example, middle C has a frequency of 256 Hz.

If you know the wavelength and the frequency of the wave you can work out how fast it is moving.

You have probably come across the words frequency and wavelength when tuning a radio.

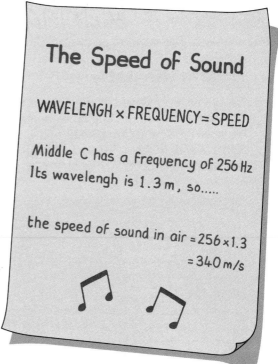

The Speed of Sound

WAVELENGH × FREQUENCY = SPEED

Middle C has a frequency of 256 Hz
Its wavelengh is 1.3 m, so.....

the speed of sound in air = 256 × 1.3
= 340 m/s

1. A note has a frequency of 40 Hz. Assuming that the speed of sound in air is 340 m/s, what is the wavelength of the note?

2. Sound waves travel at 1500 m/s in water. What will be the wavelength of waves carrying the sound of the above note through water?

3. Make a list of the wavelength and frequency of 6 different radio stations.

4. Graham did the question above. He multiplied the wavelength and frequency of his favourite radio station and was surprised when it did not come to 340 m/s. Write a short note to him, explaining his confusion. (Think about what the radio *is actually* receiving.)

4 Making music

Noting the pattern

If you have ever played all the notes on a piano in sequence, you will have noticed that the sounds form a pattern. The notes repeat themselves after 8 white keys, but at a higher **pitch**. Because the sounds are 8 notes apart, we call this an *octave* (from the Latin 'octo', meaning eight). Any note that is one octave higher than another will be exactly double the frequency of the same lower note.

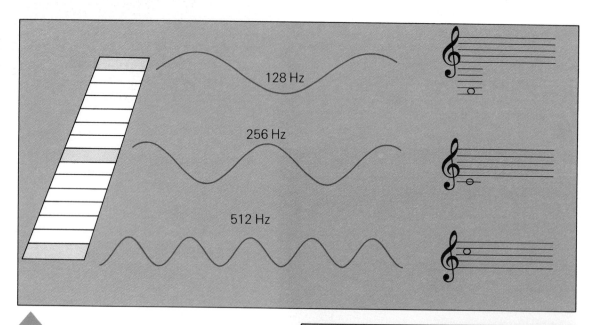

These notes are all 'C's'. Each one is an octave apart – the frequency is doubled exactly each octave.

Agreeing the pitch

The most important thing in music is not how precise the pitch is, but how the notes relate to one another – so they sound correct relative to each other. Orchestras have agreed to use a scale where the note A shown in the diagram has a frequency of 440 Hz, instead of 442 Hz. All the other notes are then adjusted accordingly.

It takes a very highly trained ear to detect a difference between middle C on the scientific scale (256 Hz) and middle C on the concert pitch scale (262 Hz). As long as the relationship between the notes on the two scales is the same, most people would not notice the difference.

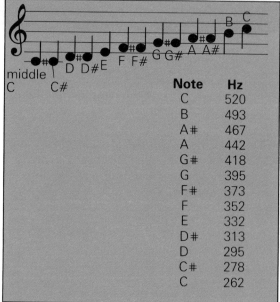

Note	Hz
C	520
B	493
A#	467
A	442
G#	418
G	395
F#	373
F	352
E	332
D#	313
D	295
C#	278
C	262

These are the frequencies for the white and black key notes on a piano. The frequencies on this scale have been slightly adjusted to make the relationship easier to follow. Can you spot the relationship?

Same note, different sound

Each musical note has its own frequency. But why do instruments playing the same note sound different? And how can an instrument like this synthesiser produce the sounds of so many different instruments?

To answer these questions we must look again at sound waves. When a note is played on an instrument, many different waves are produced at the same time. These all have different amplitudes and frequencies.

The lowest frequency wave usually has the biggest amplitude. As it is the loudest it dominates the sound, and so is called the **fundamental** frequency.

High frequencies are known as **overtones** or **harmonics**. These combine with the fundamental frequency to give a waveform which is characteristic for one particular instrument.

On the synthesiser shown, sound 37 is the saxophone. When this sound is selected the computer generates waves of this shape. The frequency of these waveforms is controlled by the girl playing the keyboard. The amplitude of the waveforms is under the control of her father, who has just turned the volume down!

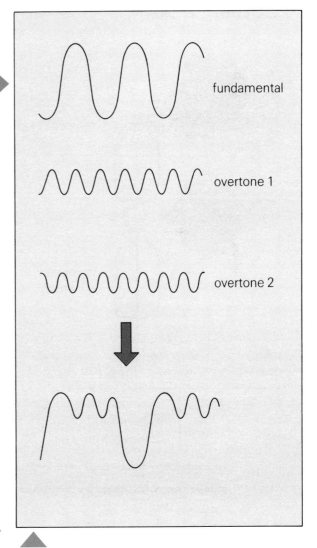

The waves generated on the synthesiser produce the characteristic sound of a saxophone.

1 Why is middle C given as 256 Hz on the top diagram on the opposite page and 262 Hz on the bottom diagram?

2 Work out the frequency of the next two notes on the concert pitch scale on the opposite page.

3 In the diagram of the saxophone's sound, the overtones have been combined with the fundamental to produce a waveform. Draw a diagram to show how the waveform would appear if the fundamental was combined with overtone 1 only.

4 Design a poster for a music shop to show how a synthesiser can generate the sounds of many different instruments.

5 Getting in rhythm

In the swing!

Have you ever pushed anyone on a swing? If you get into a rhythm, it doesn't take a lot of effort. It's a matter of timing – giving little pushes at the right frequency soon builds up a large amplitude of swing.

Any object that can vibrate has a natural frequency at which it vibrates. Forcing vibrations at the same frequency can build up very large amplitudes. This effect is known as **resonance** which means re-sounding (sounding again and again).

Bottling it up

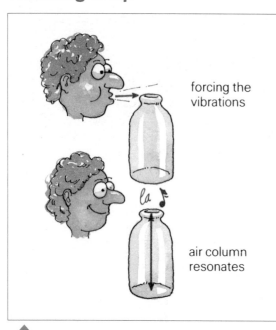

forcing the vibrations

la

air column resonates

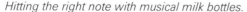

Hitting the right note with musical milk bottles.

The swing has its own natural frequency. By pushing, you build up the amplitude. You are forcing the vibrations of the swing.

You can make the air in a bottle resonate. If you blow across the top of a bottle, the air inside vibrates. It vibrates at the natural frequency for the column of air in the bottle, and you can hear this as a note. If you sing a note into a milk bottle it forces the air inside to vibrate (**forced vibrations**). If you sing the same note as the natural frequency, these vibrations reinforce the natural vibrations of the air column. Your original note will be amplified. It will resonate.

This effect is used in wind instruments, such as the flute. The natural frequency of the air column is varied by changing the length of the air column by opening and closing different holes.

A player can alter the sound of the note by changing the pitch of their own playing.

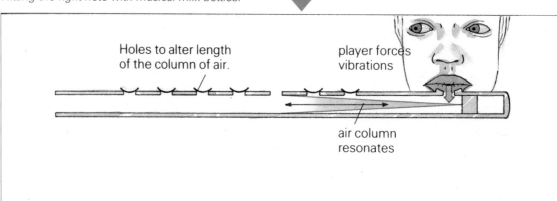

Holes to alter length of the column of air.

player forces vibrations

air column resonates

Unhelpful resonance

If you buy a pair of loudspeakers for a stereo system, the makers recommend that you fix them firmly to the wall or stand. The reason for this is resonance – if the speakers are not fixed they are free to vibrate. Any sound that coincided with the natural vibration would cause a large amount of shaking and unwanted noise.

You are also advised to leave a gap between the wall and the speaker – again to avoid resonance. A thin column of air caught between the wall and a speaker that is too close can cause unwanted amplification due to resonance.

Resonance can also cause vibration problems in cars. Any loose fittings in a car are free to vibrate – as the speed of the engine changes, so does the frequency of the vibrations it makes. At one particular speed the engine vibrations will coincide with the natural frequency and cause loose objects to resonate.

Large structures can be shattered by resonance effects. Suspension bridges are free to vibrate, so care must be taken to avoid any forcing vibrations that might cause resonance. The Tacoma Narrows bridge in the USA collapsed when gusting winds coincided with its natural frequency.

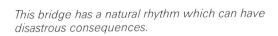
This bridge has a natural rhythm which can have disastrous consequences.

1 Make a list of times when resonance is helpful, and list of times when it must be avoided.

2 Why does the glove compartment door on my car rattle when I'm going at 50 mph?

3 Why do soldiers break step (stop marching) when going over a suspension bridge?

6 What a noise!

Stop that noise!

Have you ever been kept awake by the sound of a clock ticking? Or water gurgling in pipes? It may not be very loud, but **noise** is any sound that you would prefer not to hear. Noise can make life very unpleasant. What is noisy and what is acceptable can be a matter of opinion, but we *can* measure how loud the sound is. Very loud sounds can damage our ears.

Machinery, personal stereos and discos can all be loud enough to do damage. Most damaging of all are sudden increases in sound, such as explosions.

It is important to control noise so that it does not cause physical damage. Noise can distract people and make it difficult for them to concentrate on tasks. Noise can also be very stressful, and people who live or work in noisy environments may become ill.

People need ear protection where there is loud noise such as machinery in use or low flying aircraft or school corridors!

Measuring sound

Sound levels are measured in **decibels** using noise level meters. The usual range is from 40 dB, which is very quiet to 100 dB, which is very loud.

The sound of someone talking, measured from about 1 metre away, is about 55 decibels. In a class with everyone talking the level goes up to 90 decibels the same as a noisy factory. In fact, exposure to this noise level for eight hours a day can damage hearing.

Levels of 110 dB can damage hearing in as little as 2 minutes. This noise level is often found at rock concerts.

The decibel scale is a logarithmic scale, which means that an increase of about 3 decibels actually doubles the amount of sound energy. So reducing a sound from 87 to 81 decibels (a drop of 6 dB) means there is only ¼ of the noise there was before! Small reductions in decibels are well worth having.

Getting away from it all

Paul noticed that the sound of the vacuum cleaner was unbearable if he stood right over it, but that as he moved away, the noise became quieter.

He checked his observations with a sound sensor connected to a computer. The table gives his results.

Distance from cleaner	Noise level
10 cm	101 dB
20 cm	95 dB
40 cm	89 dB
80 cm	83 dB
160 cm	77 dB

While he had the system at home, he checked some ideas for quietening his pebble polishing machine.
These are the results he got:
Machine on its own 98 dB
Machine on foam base 95 dB
With a box round it 86 dB
With a foam lining in the box 81 dB
With a lid on the box 77 dB

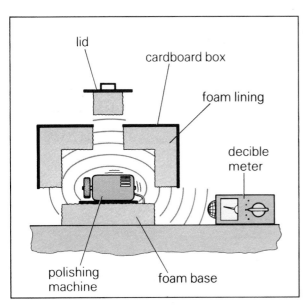

1 What are the worst sources of noise pollution in your area? What could be done about them?

2 Sara put a carpet in her car which reduced the noise level from 86 dB to 80 dB. How much did this reduce the sound energy?

3 If the noise level in a classroom goes up from 56 dB to 90 dB how much does the sound energy increase?

4 Plot the results of Paul's vacuum cleaner investigation on a graph.
   a What would you expect the noise level to be at 120 cm?
   b Where would you expect to find a noise level of 92 dB?
   c Without using the graph, can you predict what the noise level would be at 320 cm?

5 In Paul's second investigation
   a which step had the greatest effect on reducing noise?
   b how much did this step reduce sound energy?
   c how much did the insulation reduce the sound energy overall?

7 Making sound louder

Play it loud

A Karaoke party! To **amplify** the sound, a microphone is connected to an amplifier and a loudspeaker . . .

How it works . . . the microphone

The microphone works using the scientific principle that

an electric current will be induced (*started*) **in a wire that moves in a magnetic field** (See **Electricity in Action**).

The microphone has a small coil of wire that can move in and out of a circular magnet. The coil is attached to flexible material at the front of the microphone.

● When sound waves hit the microphone, they make the flexible material vibrate.
● This in turn makes the wire coil vibrate.
● When the coil vibrates it moves in and out of the circular magnet.
● This movement starts an electric current.

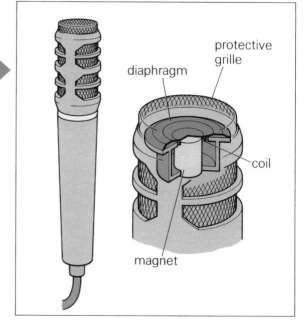

The electric current that is induced is very small. It is constantly changing, depending on how much of the coil is in the magnet (which depends on the sound waves vibrating the flexible material). This small, fluctuating current is made larger by the electronic circuitry in the amplifier. This larger current is then fed to the loudspeaker . . . . .

The loudspeaker

The loudspeaker reverses the processes that occur in the microphone. The loudspeaker works using the scientific principle that:

an electric current moving through a wire produces a magnetic effect (See **Electricity in Action**).

A very simple loudspeaker is shown in the diagram. It has a coil of wire wrapped around a paper tube. One end of the tube is connected to a cone of stiff paper, the other end fits over a permanent magnet.

● The coil of wire becomes an electromagnet when a current passes through it.
● As the current varies, the strength of the electromagnet changes. The current varies because it is coming from the microphone.
● As the strength of the electromagnet changes, the paper tube will move towards, or away from, the permanent magnet.
● As the paper tube moves, it causes the paper cone to vibrate.
● The vibration of the paper cone causes air movements. These air movements are sound waves.

So the original sounds picked up by the microphone have been reproduced at the loudspeaker. The amplitude of the sound waves at the loudspeaker is controlled by how much the electrical current is increased by the amplifier – most amplifiers have a volume control so that the sound can be adjusted. You can read more about this in **Electricity in Action**, **Spread 10.**

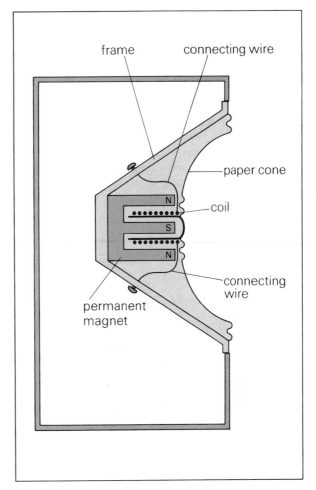

1 Draw a separate diagram for each of the 4 points in the explanation of the moving coil microphone.

2 Why doesn't the microphone require a power source?

3 Draw a small diagram to illustrate each of the 5 points in the explanation of the loudspeaker.

4 These graphs show how well three different types of cassette recorder speakers amplify sound in the range 20 kHz (bass) to 50 kHz (treble).
  a Which amplifies best in the treble region?
  b Which amplifies best in the bass?
  c Which type would you choose? Why?

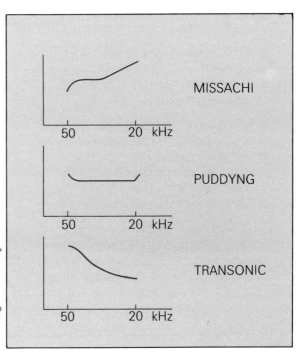

8 Useful sound

High frequency sound

Ultrasound – sound above a frequency of 20 000 Hz – can be put to good use. It can be produced by electronic systems and travels well through many solids and liquids. Ultrasound reflections can be used to build images of things we cannot usually see. Very loud ultrasound at high pressures can also be used in industry to clean or remove objects.

Looking at baby

Probably the most widely known use of ultrasound is in **scanning** a foetus in the pregnant mother's womb. It is very useful for doctors to be able to check on the baby's growth and development. Other methods of seeing inside the body (for example, using X-rays) might harm the delicate foetus whereas the use of ultrasound is virtually harmless to baby and mother.

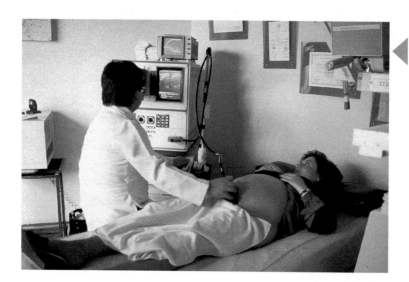

By using ultrasound equipment you can have a good look at the foetus without harming mother or baby.

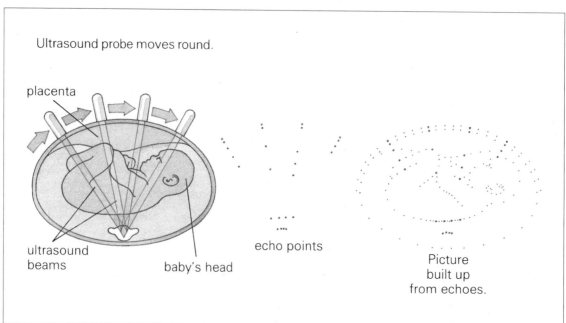

Ultrasound probe moves round.

placenta

ultrasound beams

baby's head

echo points

Picture built up from echoes.

Finding faults

As ultrasound travels well through solids it can be used to find areas in the middle of solids which are irregular. This technique is used widely in industry, to find flaws in welds or casts. Early detection of such flaws can be very important in structures such as bridges or aeroplanes.

The same idea is used by dentists in searching for cavities in teeth. The pattern of ultrasound reflections from a tooth with a hole in it will be different from the pattern from a healthy tooth. These differences can be built into an image of the cavity in the diseased tooth.

Seeing under water

As ultrasound travels well through water, its reflection, or echoes can be built into images of what is under water. This technique is used by trawlers to detect shoals of fish, by submarines for underwater navigation and by surveying ships to map the sea-bed.

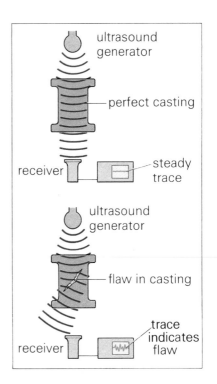

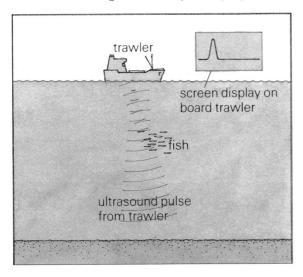

Shake and destroy!

High powered ultrasound can be used to shake and destroy objects. This technique is used in medicine to remove kidney stones and bloodclots, without having to open the patient surgically. The same idea is used to clean areas in factories and hospitals that have to be completely sterile.

1 Write a leaflet that can be given to a pregnant woman before she has an ultrasound scan. Your leaflet should explain why the process is useful and re-assure her that it will not harm either herself or her baby.

2 Make a poster showing the different uses of ultrasound.

3 Find out more about the use of ultrasound in industries and hospitals near you.

9 Talking on the telephone

When I'm calling you

A **telephone** combines both a microphone and a loudspeaker. When you use the telephone, your speech is converted to electrical signals by the microphone. These electrical signals are transmitted through cables to the receiver. Electrical signals coming the other way arrive at the loudspeaker in the earpiece. This converts the signals into sound that you can hear.

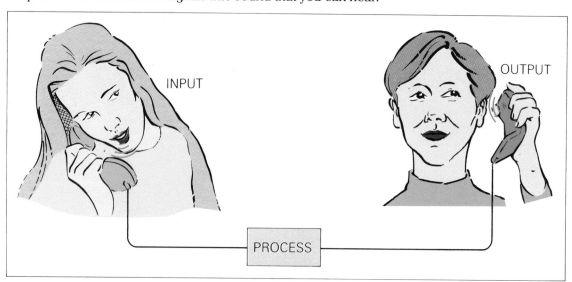

We can think of this system as having an **input** followed by a **process**, followed by an **output**. The input is speaking into the telephone, the output is the speech at the other end. The process is the movement of electrical signals along the wire.

Most communication systems involve **transducers** at the input and output stages. Transducers are devices which transform energy. In this example, the microphone is the input transducer, while the loudspeaker in the earpiece is the output transducer. You can read more about this in the **Electricity in Action, Spread 10.**

Carrying the message

Many telephone communication systems have now switched to using optical fibres instead of copper cables. In optical fibres light is used to carry the messages instead of electricity in cables.

There are a number of advantages in this:

● light travels very fast, so the fibres carry the signals much faster than copper cables.

● signals travelling along copper wires fade. They need amplifying every 4 kilometres. Although signals in optical fibres fade as well, as only need boosting every 100 km.

● electrical signals are often interfered with by other electrical equipment.

● optical fibre cables are cheaper and lighter. Only 0.01 kg of glass is needed for each km of cable – the equivalent electrical cable requires 30 kg of copper per metre!

How do optical fibres work?

The input and output of a fibre optic system are the same as for an electrical system. The input transducer **modulates** (changes) light waves according to the pattern of sound waves. The modulated light waves are reflected along the glass fibre cable. The modulated light waves are then converted back into sound at the output transducer.

As optical fibres can be made very thin and very flexible they can be used as part of a system for seeing inside someones body without the need for surgery. The fibres can be passed down through the mouth and into the stomach or other appropriate organs – this is a very useful medical advance.

The light ray is reflected back and forth inside the optical fibre.

The use of optical fibres in telephone systems has many advantages over the use of copper cables.

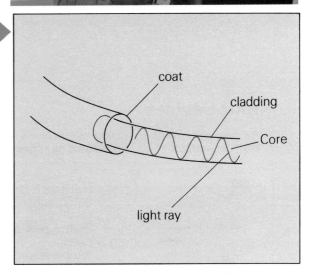

1. Draw a diagram of two people talking via a string telephone.
   Label on your diagram:
   a the Input Transducer
   b the Output Transducer
   c the part of the system where the signal is processed.

2. How often do you use the telephone.
   What is the average time that you and your friends spend on the telephone each week?
   How much does this cost?

3. Draw flow charts to compare an optical fibre telephone system with an electrical copper cable system.

4. A telephone company wants to dig up the roads in a town to replace copper cable with fibre optic cable. Prepare a leaflet to give to people explaining why the disruption is necessary and how the new system works.

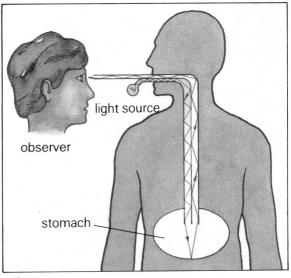

Taking a closer look using optical fibres.

10 Electronic systems and you

'Who are you calling a dishwasher?'

What's the similarity between you and a dishwasher? More than the obvious answer of 'we're both made to do the dishes!'

● You both collect information – this is the input (**page 114**).
● You both process (**page 114**) that *information* – your brain does this for you, but the dishwasher uses a microprocessor chip.
● You both *do* something as a result – this is the output (**page 114**)

Input devices

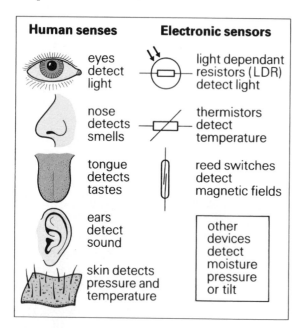

Human senses	Electronic sensors
eyes detect light	light dependant resistors (LDR) detect light
nose detects smells	thermistors detect temperature
tongue detects tastes	reed switches detect magnetic fields
ears detect sound	other devices detect moisture pressure or tilt
skin detects pressure and temperature	

You collect information through your sense organs. Electronic systems collect their information from a range of sensors too. The simplest message that these sensors can send to the microprocessor is one of two signals: we represent a 'high' or 'on' signal by 1, and a 'low' or 'off' signal by 0.

A range of outputs

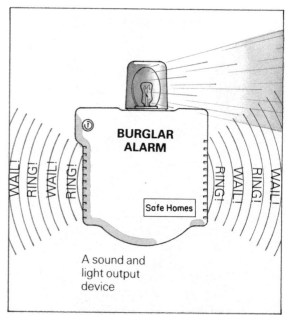

BURGLAR ALARM

Safe Homes

A sound and light output device

Once our brain has processed the information, our 'output' is often some kind of movement – smiling, running, eating, speaking. A microprocessor can activate any device to which it is connected – the 'output' may be turning on or off lights, motors, heating coils, solenoids, etc.

Processing information

'It's dark so I'll switch on the light' seems a simple decision. For an electronic system, even this decision would need some processors. A 'low' (= 'light off') signal would have to be turned to a 'high' (= 'on') signal to switch on the light. This type of simple inverting processor is call a NOT-gate.

'If it's dark or if someone asks me, I'll switch on the light' requires a different decision. More often, signals from different inputs have to be *combined*. An OR-gate will send a high-output signal if *either* of its inputs goes high.

An AND-gate will only send a high output if both its inputs are high. These gates make logical decisions, so they are known as logic gates.

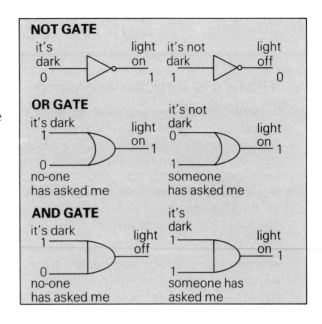

Remembering decisions

The simple **logic gates** shown above have no memory. If you used only these gates to build a burglar alarm for your front door, the alarm would ring when the door opened, but stop as soon as it closed!

Fortunately special gates called bistable gates overcome the problem. Bistable gates have two stable states – this gives them a simple memory. If an alarm sensor sends a signal to the 'SET' input, even for a split second, the gate remembers it, and the alarm will continue to ring until a signal is send to the 'RESET' input. This is just an electronic version of a common light switch – it stays 'on' until you actively turn it 'off' by pushing the other side.

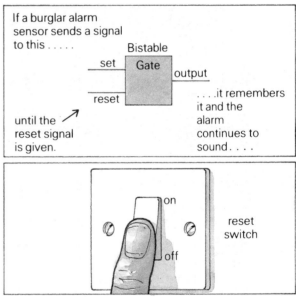

---

1 Draw strip cartoons to illustrate the decisions about turning on the light that are described in the above section 'Processing information'.

2 Draw a NOT gate to illustrate the inputs and outputs of a system that switches on a heating system when it is cold.

3 Draw an OR gate to illustrate the inputs and outputs of a system that allows TV channels to be changed either by a button on the set or by a remote control unit.

4 Draw an AND gate to illustrate the inputs and outputs of a system that only lets water into a washing machine if the programme has been set and the door has been closed.

11 Full to capacity

There's a Pelican crossing!

Sometimes an electronic system has to do something for a period of time and then stop. A good example of such a system is a Pelican crossing. The Pelican crossing normally shows a red display, meaning 'Don't Cross'. When it receives a suitable input, the circuit changes the display to green and gives a warble signal. This lasts for a short time and then the diusplay changes back to red.

This system is said to be **monostable**. It has two possible states. The red display is the **stable** state. The input forces the circuit into the other state (the green display), but it does not stay there. After a time delay it drops back into the stable state – the red display – again

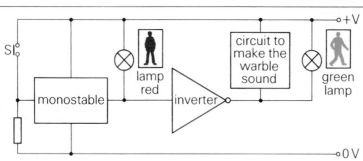

When operated the system for a pelican crossing changes the lights from red (stable) to green (for a limited time) and then back to red again.

Causing a delay

The part of a monostable circuit that causes the time delay is the **capacitor**. It is an electronic component that can be 'filled with charge'. It takes time for the capacitor to fill with charge, expecially if the capacitor is connected to a **resistor**.

As the current flows into the uncharged capacitor, the voltage across the capacitor gets bigger. The process can be reversed by connecting a conductor to the capacitor – a current will flow from the capacitor and the potential difference will fall. You can read more about this in **Electricity in Action**.

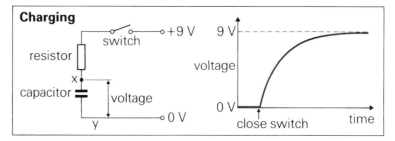

a   When the switch is closed the capacitor begins to charge up. As it does so the voltage between X and Y increases. The time taken depends on the size of the capacitor and the size of the resistor.

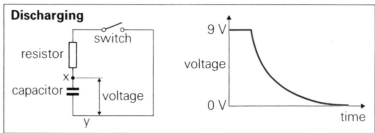

b   A conductor is now connected across the capacitor. When the switch is closed the capacitor discharges, and the voltage drops to zero. The capacitor and resistor are once again variables in the time taken for this to happen.

Changing times

The time it takes for a capacitor to charge up or to discharge depends on two things which may vary (**variables**):

1 the size of the capacitor

2 the size of the resistor.

The bigger either of these variables, the longer the time delay.

R (kΩ)	C (µF)	T (s)
100	10	1
500	110	5
500	50	25
500	100	50

More microphones

Capacitors are also used in some microphones. These are known as **condenser microphones**. In this type of microphone two metal plates form a capacitor. A small battery is connected across them. The top plate vibrates when sound waves reach it. As the plate vibrates the distance to the other plate changes, and so the value of the capacitor changes.

The changes in the capacitor result in changes in the potential difference across the resistor. The change in voltage becomes the output signal from the microphone. The signal is often small and needs to be amplified.

1 Copy the block diagram of the Pelican Crossing and say what each part of the system does.

2 A Pelican Crossing near an old peoples home displays green for twenty five seconds. This is a bit short for some people to cross. Suggest two ways in which the system could be altered to double the crossing time.

3 Compare this type of microphone to the moving coil type shown on spread 7. List the differences between them.

4 What other types of microphone can you name?

5 What are the advantages and disadvantages of the different types of microphones? You could make a chart to show these.

The built-in microphones on cassette recorders are usually of the condenser type.

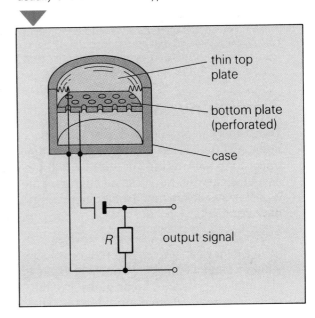

12 Feedback from transistors

Simple, but effective

A **transistor** is a component which can be used as a simple electronic switch.

Transistors have three leads, the **base**, the **collector** and the **emitter**. The base is used as the input and the collector as the output. When current flows into the base, either from a sensor or from another circuit, the current at the collector will be controlled.

The diagrams show how a transistor can be used to switch a circuit on and off. ▼

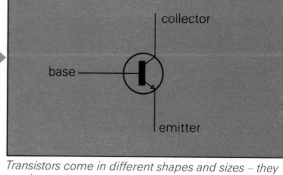

Transistors come in different shapes and sizes – they can be made very small indeed and are an important part of the microcircuitry in computers.

▼

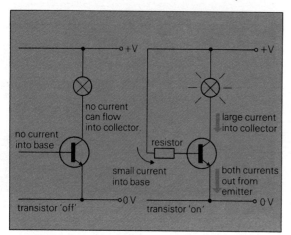

▲

Allowing current into the base has the effect of closing the switch so that current can flow. The resistor makes sure that only a small current flows into the base. A large current would cause the transistor to overheat and fail.

Amplifying the effect

Transistors can also be used to amplify an input. A current is fed to the base so that the transistor is halfway on. This current is known as a **bias current**. Now a small change in the input will result in a much larger increase in the output.

Transistors are called **analogue devices** because they can give any current or voltage within a particular range. Variable resistors are also analogue devices. **Logic gates**, like the ones on **spread 10** are **digital devices**. They only have two outputs – on or off (sometimes these are referred to as high or low).

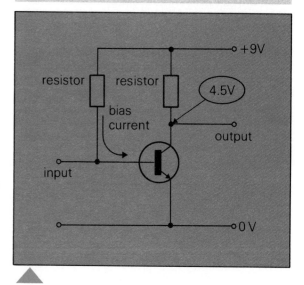

▲

Using a bias current to amplify an input.

The right feedback

Transistors can be made to stabilise the flow of electricity. In the diagram below, an increase in current through the base will lead to a drop in voltage at point A. This will decrease the current to the base, and so decrease the current to point A. This in turn leads to an increase in voltage at A.

The current through the transistor quickly becomes very stable, balanced at the point where there is no increase or decrease in voltage. This is called **negative feedback**.

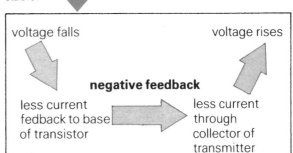

A change in voltage produces the opposite change in the system. These changes keep the overall current stable.

voltage falls

voltage rises

negative feedback

less current feedback to base of transistor

less current through collector of transmitter

Feedback consists of sending part of the output signal back to the input. This can have two effects:

a the feedback signal is added to the input signal so the output becomes much larger.

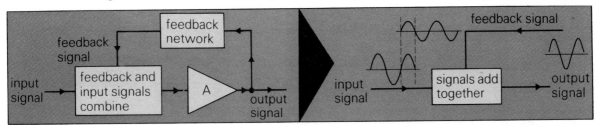

b the feedback signal cancels out part of the input signal so the output becomes smaller.

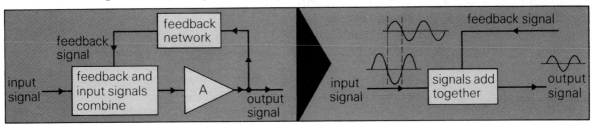

Making use of feedback

Negative feedback is very useful in controlling currents. Positive feedback is normally avoided as it produces large and unstable effects. Feedback is not only found in electronic systems. In living organisms it is important that the conditions inside the body are correctly balanced all the time. Control of these conditions – such as temperature, blood, sugar levels etc. is achieved by negative feedback mechanisms in the body.

1 When you use a transistor as a switch, which leads are used for input and output?

2 A streetlamp was set to switch on when the voltage from a light sensor exceeded 1.0 V. During one evening the output from the light sensor changed as follows:

Time	6.00	6.30	7.00	7.30	8.00	8.30
Output	0.2 V	0.2 V	0.5 V	0.8 V	1.5 V	1.5 V

Draw a graph of these results and use it to estimate the time the light came on.

3 A microphone is connected to a loudspeaker so that a speech can be amplified. When the microphone is moved close to the loudspeaker a loud and unpleasant screech is heard. This is because of feedback. Use the description of feedback above to explain what is happening. Is this positive or negative feedback?

4 Give an example of a negative feedback system in the human body. Look at the modules **Humans as Organisms and Maintenance of Life**.

13 Recording sound

Storing the sound . . .

Sound waves can be represented as a pattern. If we can store that pattern, we can make a record of the sound that made it. These two pages look at some systems for storing and reproducing sound patterns. More information about how electromagnets work is given in **Electricity in Action**.

. . . on records

One way of storing a sound wave pattern is to cut a groove into plastic. The shape of the groove depends on the shape of the sound wave. This is the way records are made.

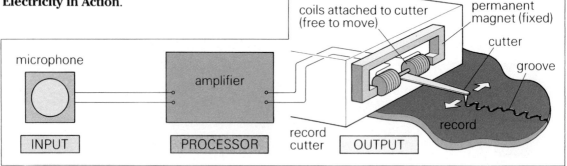

. . . on tapes

Another way is to store the pattern as a pattern of magnetic particles. The amount of magnetic particles depends on the shape of the sound wave. This is the way tapes are made.

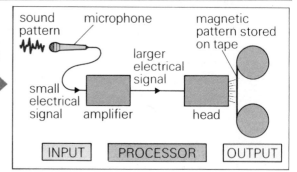

. . . on films

A third way is to produce a pattern of light and dark bands. The darkness of the bands depends on the shape of the sound wave. This is the way sound tracks are made for films.

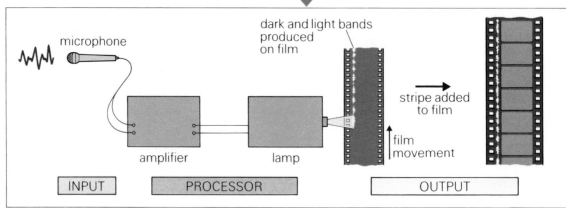

1 These methods of storing sound rely on electromagnets. What happens to the patterns as the current from the amplifier?
a increases? **b** decreases?

Reproducing stored sound . . .

Reproducing sound from a record, tape or film means reversing the process that stored the original sound.

. . . on records

The groove in this record is cut to give two types of movement: side to side and up and down. The movement produces varying electric current, which is amplified and sent to a loudspeaker. This gives the sound that you can hear. The two movements give two sounds, producing stereo effects.

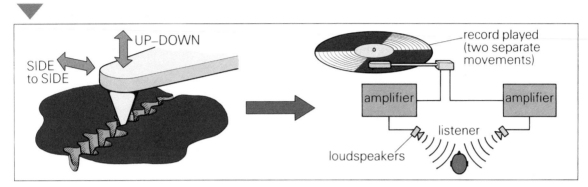

. . . on tapes

When a tape is played back, the magnetic pattern passes through the tape head. This produces a varying current which is amplified and sent to a loudspeaker.

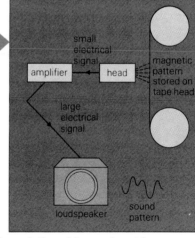

. . . on films

When a film passes through a projector, a light shines against the sound track. As the sound track is a pattern of light and dark bands, the amount of light that shines through the sound track will vary. The variation in light is used to produce a varying electric current. The current is amplified and sent to a loudspeaker.

The light shines through the white varying stripes on the right to produce an electric current which is converted into sound.

The large square holes on both sides engage in the teeth of cogs which move the film past the light source.

2 Draw flow diagrams to show the inputs, outputs and processes of:
   a recording music on a tape.
   b reproducing music from a record.
   c reproducing sound from a film.

3 Make a list of the advantages and disadvantages of the different ways of storing and reproducing sound shown on these two pages.

14 Digital sound

It's groovy!

Records and tapes store sounds in patterns that imitate the original sound wave. The grooves of a record or the pattern of magnetic particles is *like* the original, so this type of recording is known as **analogue** recording. (An **analogy** is something that is *like* something else).

The photograph shows the groove cut in a record, and how it has bumps like the original sound wave. It also shows some of the disadvantages of this way of storing sound – the white marks are tiny specks of dust which can get into the groove and distort the pattern. The groove can also become scratched and worn by the movement of the stylus through it.

Digital recording

When sound is recorded digitally, the height of the sound wave is **sampled** – it is measured and recorded thousands of times a second. The height is recorded in binary code, as a series of 1s and 0s. Recording in 1s and 0s is known as **digital** recording. How well this process works depends on how often the wave form is sampled. Modern digital recording samples a sound wave 40 000 times a second!

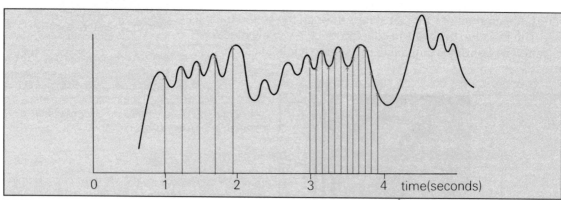

Sampling a signal from a microphone.

1 Mark the heights sampled in red onto a piece of graph paper. Without looking at the book, join the red crosses with a line. Do the same with the blue crosses.
How well do your lines represent the different parts of the sound wave sampled?

2 What sampling rate is represented by
a the red crosses
b the blue crosses?

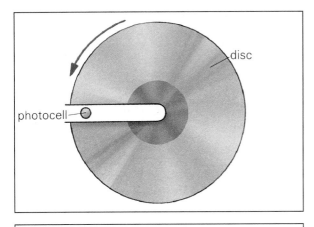

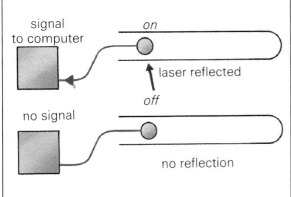

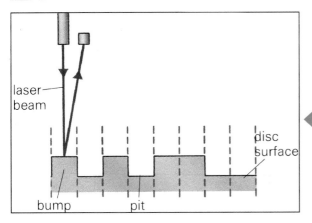

laser beam

bump   pit

disc surface

Compact discs

Compact discs make use of the technique of digital recording. A compact disc is made up of raised surfaces and pits. The raised parts represent the 1s in binary code, the pits represent the 0s. A laser beam is shone at the disc and this reflects from the raised surfaces, but *not* from the pits.

As the disc spins round the laser beam is either reflected or is not reflected by each part of the disc. So the photo-cell is either switched *on* or *off.* This information is then sent to a loudspeaker system which reconverts the digital information into sound. With 40 000 pieces of information each second about the shape of the wave the sound quality is very high. The other advantage of the system is that nothing ever touches the raised surfaces and the pits, so they don't get worn away. A transparent protective coating means that the disc is kept free of dirt and scratches.

As the disc spins round a photocell detects whether the laser is reflected or not at any instant. The photocell switches an electrical signal on each time the laser is reflected and off each time it is not reflected. The pattern made by these electrical signals is interpreted into very high quality sound.

3 The binary code represented in the diagram is 10101100. Draw compact disc surfaces that represent the following binary codes
11001101
01000011
11100110

4 Draw a flow diagram showing how digital sound is recorded and reproduced.

5 A local electrical store has found that its sales of CD equipment are falling off. Design a poster that explains why CDs offer better sound reproduction for display in the shop.

15 For you to do

1 Sound can vary in its pitch and its loudness. This diagram shows how both pitch and loudness vary for some different sounds.

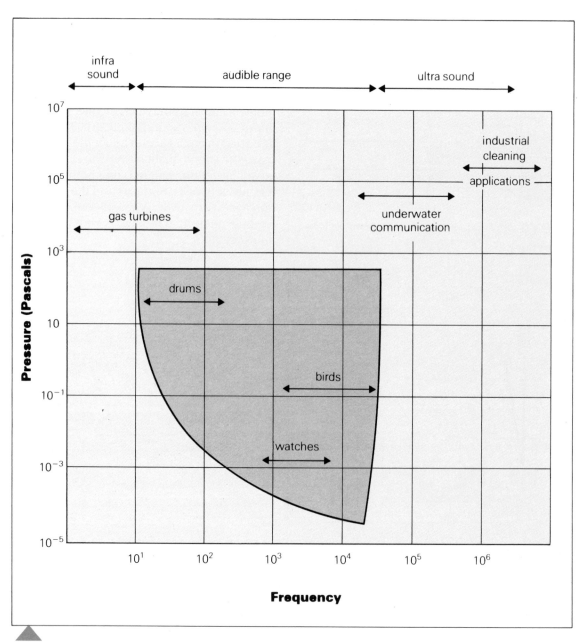

The shaded area shows the sounds we can normally hear.

a What is the loudest sound shown on the diagram?
b What is the loudest sound that we can hear shown on the diagram?
c What is the softest sound that we can hear shown on the diagram?
d What is the lowest pitch sound shown on the diagram?
e What is the lowest pitched sound that we can hear shown on the diagram?
f What does the diagram tell us about how well we can hear sounds of different pitch?

2 This table shows how sound of different wavelengths is absorbed by air. The higher the figure shown, the more of the sound that is absorbed. The greater the distance the sound travels, the greater the amount absorbed.

Frequency (Hertz)	Absorption (dB/100m)
125	0.06
250	0.16
500	0.35
1000	1.24
2000	4.20
4000	10.80

a Display the results in the table graphically

b Use these figures to explain why traffic noise sounds like a low-pitched rumble when you stand in the middle of a large park.

c A foghorn is a device that lets out a loud, low-pitched note as a warning to other ships when fog makes it difficult to see. Why is the note low pitched?

3 The chart below is from a *Consumers Association* survey of stereo cassette recorders. Use the data to write a short report for the school magazine, picking out points of comparison between the recorders. Your report should recommend one 'best buy' in the single tape deck category, and one in the twin tape deck category. You should also give brief reasons for your choice.

	Price	Size hxwxd	Weight	Battery running costs	Maximum volume	General features	Radio features	FM reception	FM sound quality	AM reception	AM sound quality	Features	Pre-recorded cassettes	Recording from radio
	£	cm	kg											
● ONE CASSETTE DECK														
Cathay SRC635Q (China)	30	14×37×9	2.1	◪	☐	BQ	–	☐	☐	◪	◪	a	◪	■
Hitachi TRK-640E (Singapore)	40	16×50×12	2.7	◪	☐	BIT	lsz	◪	☐	◪	◪	–	☐	☐
Panasonic RX-FS400 (Singapore)	45	14×45×15	2.8	◪	◪	BHT	lsz	☐	◪	■	☐	–	☐	☐
Phillips AQ 5192 (Malaysia) [1]	40	14×41×12	2.2	◪	☐	BH	lz	☐	☐	◪	☐	a	☐	☐
Realistic SCR-90 (Hong Kong)	40	13×35×8	1.5	◪	☐	B	–	☐	☐	◪	◪	–	◪	■
Sharp QT-250A (Malaysia)	40	14×45×14	3.0	◪	☐	EHT	z[2]	◪	◪	◪	☐	a	◪	☐
Sony CFS201L (Malaysia)	45	15×48×14	2.9	◪	◪	BHT	lstz	◪	◪	■	☐	–	◪	☐
Sony CFS903L (Taiwan)	80	20×44×13	2.6	◪	◪	BHTW	lstz	◪	◪	◪	☐	mr	◪	◪
● TWO CASSETTE DECKS														
Aiwa CS-WN30 (China)	60	15×54×13	3.4	◪	☐	BHT	l	☐	◪	☐	☐	p	◪	◪
Akai AJ-W259 (Taiwan)	70	16×56×17	3.5	◪	☐	BHS	lz	☐	◪	◪	◪	ap	◪	☐
Boots SRR33T (China)	40	14×50×12	2.9	◪	◪	BEHT	z	☐	☐	◪	☐	p	☐	◪
Crown SZ-K230 (China)	40	14×50×14	3.0	◪	☐	BT	z	☐	◪	☐	◪	p	◪	◪
Hitachi TRK-W220E (Singapore)	60	15×54×12	3.3	■	☐	BHT	lsz	☐	◪	◪	☐	p	◪	◪
JVC RC-W210 (Malaysia)	80	16×62×17	4.9	☐	◪	EHQ	z	◪	◪	■	◪	ap	◪	◪
Panasonic RX-FT500 (Singapore)	60	15×56×15	3.7	◪	☐	BHIT	lsz	◪	◪	■	☐	ap	■	◪
Phillips AW 7392 (Austria)	70	15×50×14	3.0	◪	☐	BH	lz	◪	◪	◪	☐	apr[3]	☐	◪
Saisho T292A (Korea)	40	14×52×13	3.1	◪	☐	B	z	◪	☐	◪	◪	p	☐	◪
Sanyo MW709F (Japan)	50	15×52×13	3.1	◪	☐	HT	–	☐	☐	◪	◪	a	◪	◪
Sharp WQ-268E (Malaysia)	60	14×50×13	3.0	☐	◪	EHT	lsz	◪	■	☐	◪	ap	◪	◪

[1] Model tested was AQ 5190 (not available in UK); it doesn't have long wave   [2] Mono switching on FM is automatic   [3] Autoreverse on one cassette deck only

KEY TO RATINGS	◪	◪	☐	◪	■
	best◄—			—► worst	

I.L.E.A.
MALORY SCHOOL
LAUNCELOT ROAD
DOWNHAM, BROMLEY, KENT

Photo acknowledgements

The references indicate page numbers and, where appropriate, the photo sequence.

contents page and cover: Pictor International. *pp. 98, 99, 100, 101, 105, 106, 107, 108, 109, 118, 119, 120* Steve Smyth. *p. 107* J. Allan Cash Ltd.

p.110 Robert Harding Picture Library. *p. 112* Science Photo Library/David Leah. *p. 115* British Telecommunications plc. *p. 123* Eastman Kodak Company Ltd. *p. 124* Science Photo Library/ Dr Tony Brain.